The Basics of Critical Thinking

The Basics of Critical Thinking is available in print or eBook form.

Written by
Michael Baker

Graphic Design by
Chip Dombrowski

Edited by
Patricia Gray

© 2015
THE CRITICAL THINKING CO.™
www.CriticalThinking.com
Phone: 800-458-4849 • Fax: 541-756-1758
1991 Sherman Ave., Suite 200 • North Bend • OR 97459
ISBN 978-1-60144-507-0

W9-CTC-081

Table of Contents

About the Author

Michael Baker has been president of The Critical Thinking Co.™ for over 25 years. He majored in philosophy at the University of Michigan for six years. He has authored or coauthored several award-winning books and software products for The Critical Thinking Co.™

What This Book Teaches

The Basics of Critical Thinking is designed to teach critical thinking skills and concepts to upper elementary through middle school students. Many workbooks claim to teach or develop critical thinking skills, but most of these products never define critical thinking or try to teach the meaning to students. This book defines and teaches critical thinking in a way students can understand and apply.

Critical thinking is "finding and evaluating evidence to try to make the best decisions." This book focuses on using critical thinking skills when making decisions and acquiring knowledge— specifically evaluating claims and arguments. Is there more to teaching critical thinking? Absolutely, but we can teach the importance of such things as being fair minded, objective, and avoiding emotional thinking without overloading the definition.

The Basics of Critical Thinking teaches critical thinking skills and concepts through a step-by-step process that provides plenty of practice. Most parents and educators would be thrilled if the students in their charge learned to identify and weigh the available evidence before making a decision, so this book focuses on those skills, and also teaches many other important critical thinking concepts.

Unlike other courses in critical thinking, this book tries to minimize the lecture time and teach students through easy-to-understand explanations, diagrams, and short engaging activities. Although this is a course in critical thinking, you can pick and choose individual lessons from the book to supplement lessons in all subjects.

At the end of the book, students are introduced to common argument forms and fallacies, but unlike many other critical thinking products, teaching the names of argument forms and fallacies is NOT the major focus of this book. There is some value in teaching students about common argument forms, but not recognizing (e.g.) an argument form by name is very seldom the cause of a bad decision. Most students and adults are not bamboozled by lengthy complex arguments; they are usually a victim of their own inability to identify and evaluate the evidence couched within a simple argument. If you examine most advertising schemes, legal trickery, and bad science, you'll nearly always find simple arguments filled with half-truths and/or inconclusive claims. The focus of this book is to teach students how to evaluate claims and arguments, so that they know how to evaluate claims and arguments in real-life situations.

The Basics of Critical Thinking establishes a basic foundation of good critical thinking skills for students to build upon the rest of their lives. Students who complete this book should be able to look at a claim and determine if it is true, probably true, false, probably false, or if they need more information to make a judgment. Students will also learn that it is their responsibility to investigate claims and arguments because to assume something is true without examining the source and the claims results in poor decisions and often regret.

The activities in this book are fun for students. This often makes it easier for teachers and parents to engage students in discussions about the activities which in turn lead to greater introspection by students about their own thinking processes.

Four Myths About Critical Thinking

Critical Thinking Is Used Mostly by Scientists

No! Scientists use critical thinking because it is the most reliable way we have found to make the best decisions. For the same reason, many parents, teachers, plumbers, historians, builders, and engineers use critical thinking to make decisions. Critical thinking is used by anyone who wants to use the best process to make decisions on what to believe and what to do. The purpose of this book is to improve your critical thinking skills and encourage you to use Critical Thinking more often—especially when you are making important decisions.

Students Don't Know Anything About Critical Thinking Without a Course in Critical Thinking

False. Nearly all students have used critical thinking to make decisions in their lives, but most do not use it consistently or skillfully. Most students don't know the meaning of critical thinking so they don't realize that they have actually used it at times to help them make a decision. Students are not practiced at identifying and evaluating evidence so their skills need development. Finally, the critical thinking process is thought of as work by many students so they avoid expending the necessary effort to carry out the process. This book is designed to teach students that critical thinking is like a detective game. It can be stimulating and FUN!

Evidence-Based Definition of Critical Thinking Conflicts With Faith-Based Beliefs

Critical thinkers come in all colors, sizes, shapes. My faith is completely compatible with an evidence-based critical thinking process because I believe I have plenty of evidence to support my beliefs (faith). Critical thinking also aids me when my beliefs are challenged because I am better equipped to analyze claims and arguments challenging my beliefs and also more skilled at defending my beliefs.

Critical Thinking Always Produces Moral/Ethical Decisions

You can find many definitions of critical thinking. Some definitions are very long and include many moral or political values such as being fair, generous, kind, honest, and open minded. Nearly all of us would agree that these are admirable traits for someone to have, but critical thinking is a decision making process—not a code of conduct or moral compass. I can think of many criminals and other bad people who have used skilled critical thinking to make decisions that helped them achieve an immoral end acceptable to their morals or lack thereof. A robber might show good critical thinking skills picking the right time and method to carry out a robbery, but poor critical thinking skills when he/she decided to rob someone in the first place, but these are two different decisions. This book does not attempt to teach morals/values or ethics.

Critical Thinking Pretest

The police are holding these four men. They believe one of these suspects stole a woman's dog from a car in a parking lot. The police interviewed three witnesses who saw the thief in the lot.

| **A** | **B** | **C** | **D** |

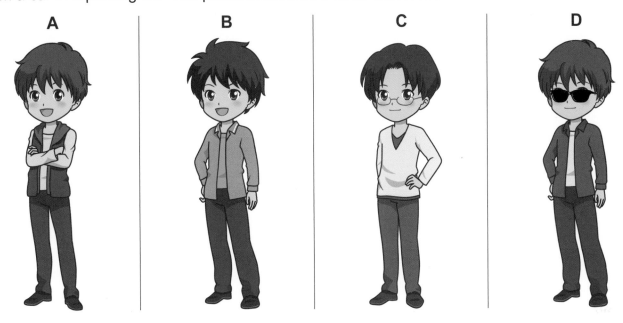

Here is how each witness described the thief:

 Witness 1: [1]The thief needed a haircut. [2]His pants were kind of dark.

 Witness 2: [3]He was looking inside the cars when he saw the tiny little dog. [4]He reached in and grabbed the dog and then stuffed it into his sweater or jacket. [5]I remember that he had on something red and something light-colored. [6]He wore a big watch on his right hand.

 Witness 3: [7]I remember seeing his brown eyes and brown or gray slacks along with his glasses. [8]His shoes were brown and he didn't wear a belt.

Circle the sentence numbers that suggest each suspect is or is not the dog thief. Next evaluate the evidence and then circle your suspect.

A	**B**	**C**	**D**
This is the thief.	This is the thief.	This is the thief.	This is the thief.
1 2 3 4	1 2 3 4	1 2 3 4	1 2 3 4
5 6 7 8	5 6 7 8	5 6 7 8	5 6 7 8
This is not the thief.	This is not the thief.	This is not the thief.	This is not the thief.
1 2 3 4	1 2 3 4	1 2 3 4	1 2 3 4
5 6 7 8	5 6 7 8	5 6 7 8	5 6 7 8

1
What Is Critical Thinking?

School and Life Are About Making the Best Decisions

It is important in school and in life to make the best decisions you can so you can live a better, happier life. All of us make two types of decisions. We decide what to believe and what to do.

What Is Critical Thinking?

Critical thinking is a way to use what you know and what you can learn to help you decide what to believe and what to do.

Critical thinking is finding and evaluating evidence to make the best decisions.

Critical thinking can be a way to learn new things, but it is not a knowledge. The best critical thinker in the world would be a terrible medical doctor if he or she didn't know a lot about the human body. Critical thinking is a way to use your knowledge and beliefs to make better decisions.

You Have Used Critical Thinking Before

Everyone has used critical thinking skills before to make a decision, but many people are not skilled at identifying and evaluating evidence. The activities in this book will improve your critical thinking skills to help you make better decisions in school and life.

Example

Look at the picture and then use your critical thinking skills to answer to the questions below.

1. The dog belongs to the man.   Yes   No   Unknown

> This could be the man's dog, but it could be a neighbor's dog or someone else's dog, so the answer is unknown.

2. The dog wants the man to take the paper.   Yes   No   Unknown

> The dog might want the man to take the paper or it could want to keep it and play with it. Have you ever had a dog that didn't want to give up a toy in its mouth? We don't know what the dog wants to do with the paper, so the answer is unknown.

The Baby Carriage

Look at the picture and then use your critical thinking skills to answer the questions below. Circle your answers.

1. Is there a baby in the carriage?

    Yes   No   Unknown

2. Is the woman pushing the carriage a mom?

    Yes   No   Unknown

3. If the woman in the picture is a mom, is this her baby carriage?

    Yes   No   Unknown

Tiger in the Tent

Look at the picture and then use your critical thinking skills to answer the questions below. Circle your answers.

1. The tracks on the ground are from a tiger.

    Yes   No   Unknown

2. There is a scared camper in the tent.

    Yes   No   Unknown

3. The tiger is still in the tent.

    Yes   No   Unknown

4. The tiger is looking for food.

    Yes   No   Unknown

The Cort House

Read the story and look for evidence in the picture to answer the questions below.

All four members of the Cort family just returned to their house after a three-day vacation visiting relatives. It started snowing last night, but stopped just before they got home. Mr. and Mrs. Cort bought a new sled on their way home and parked the car right in front of the house. All of the Cort family is in the house. The Cort family are the only people in the house. None of the Corts were carried into the house.

1. Which Cort is not in the picture?

   _____

2. If you look at the tracks in the snow, how many people are in the house?

   _____

3. If there are four members of the Cort family in the house, how could the fourth member of the family get into the house?

   _____

   _____

2
Decisions and Conclusions

Decision

A decision is anything you choose to do or believe.

Examples of Decisions

- I decided to do my homework after dinner.

- I chose to go out for the swimming team.

- After looking at the gray clouds, I decided to wear my raincoat.

- I decided to try to kick the ball over the head of the goalie.

Conclusion

A conclusion is a decision made after thinking about something.

Examples of Conclusions

- After looking at the cloudless sky, I concluded it was going to be a hot day.

- My mom looked angry so I concluded this was not the best time to ask for candy.

- I concluded this had to be a large animal after listening to it move through the brush.

- I concluded from the ringtone that my dad was calling.

Practice Problems

Write a decision and a conclusion about each picture as if you were a person in the picture.

1.

Decision   I have decided to see if this dog will chase a ball.

Conclusion   I have concluded this is not a real dog.

2.

Decision   _____

Conclusion   _____

_____

3.

Decision   _____

Conclusion _____

_____

4.

Decision   _____

Conclusion _____

_____

5.

Decision _____

Conclusion _____

_____

Look at your conclusions for 2-5. Could you make any of those decisions without considering your choices? It is hard to think of making a decision without considering two or more of your choices. Even if someone put pieces of identical candy in front of you and told you to eat your choice of the candies, you would still have to decide which one to pick up. Could you pick up one of the candies without thinking about your choice?

6. Can you make a conclusion that is not a decision? Explain the reason you believe your answer is correct.

_____

_____

_____

_____

3
Beliefs and Claims

Our beliefs are information that we <u>think</u> is true. Each of us has many, many beliefs.

<u>Examples of Beliefs</u>

- My dog is hungry.

- My mom's car has four wheels.

- The closest food store to my house is about a mile away.

- I wear a size 6 shoe.

- It will rain tomorrow.

- I'm the best math student in my class.

A claim is information that you <u>say or write</u> is true.

<u>Examples of Claims</u>

- My brother ate my desert.

- My mom's motorcycle has two wheels.

- The closest food store is less than a mile from my house.

- I wear a size 7 shoe.

- It will rain tomorrow.

- I'm the best math student in my class.

Nearly all of our claims come from our beliefs. If you believe something, you are usually willing to claim it as true, but it is possible to claim something is true even though you don't believe it. When someone knows something is not true, but claims it is true, the person is telling a lie.

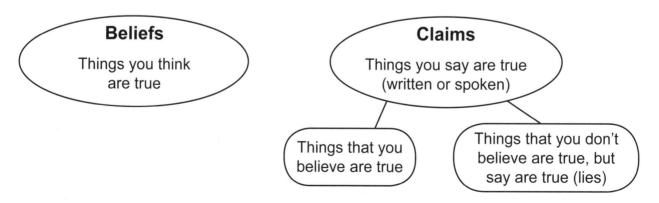

Practice Problems

Write a belief and a claim about each picture.

Belief	Claim
1. *I believe the dog dug the hole to bury the bone.*	*The dog will bury the bone to hide it from other dogs.*

Belief	Claim
2. _____ _____	_____ _____

Write a belief and a claim about each picture.

Belief   Claim

3. _____   _____

   _____   _____

Belief   Claim

4. _____   _____

   _____   _____

The Importance of Understanding Claims

If someone tries to convince you that their claim is true, it is important to make sure you understand his or her claim. If you don't understand someone's claim, you can't look for evidence to decide if it is true or false. If you can't understand a claim, you shouldn't accept it as true or false.

Not all claims are easy to understand. If the meaning of a claim is unclear, you should ask the person making the claim to explain it more clearly. If a person wants you to believe something, then it is his/her responsibility to make it clear to you. Look at this example:

She has light hair.

Is the writer claiming this about the blond girl or the gray cat?

The kitten is cute.

Which kitten is the writer talking about?

4
Finding Evidence

Always Look for Evidence

As a critical thinker, the first thing you need to do to help you make a decision is to look for evidence. Evidence is information that helps us decide if something is true or false.

Read the story below and then answer the questions to decide who got into the peanut butter and jam. Remember to find all the evidence and then think carefully about the evidence before making your decision.

Who Ate the Jam and Peanut Butter?

[1]Eddie's mom looked at Eddie and his little sister Sarah. [2]There were crumbs on the floor, and Sarah had peanut butter and jam on her chin. [3]"Who got into the peanut butter and jam without asking?" asked Eddie's mom. [4]Eddie told his mom that he didn't have any, but that Sarah had eaten the peanut butter and jam. [5]Sarah shouted, "No, I didn't!" [6]He quickly grabbed a paper towel and put some water on it so his mother could wipe Sarah's chin. [7]As Eddie handed the towel to his mother, she noticed a little peanut butter and jam on the corner of his mouth and the sleeve of his shirt.

Circle each sentence number that has evidence to support each conclusion below.

Sarah was eating the peanut butter and jam.	Eddie was eating the peanut butter and jam.
1 ② 3 ④ 5 6 7	1 2 3 4 5 6 ⑦

1. Based on all the evidence in the story, do you think Sarah was into the peanut butter and jam?

 (Yes) or No

> Sentence 2 tells us that Sarah had peanut butter and jam on her chin. Sentence 4 tells us that Eddie claims his sister ate peanut butter and jam. Both these sentences have evidence that Sarah ate peanut butter and jam. Sarah denies she ate peanut butter and jam in sentence 5. It is possible that Eddie put peanut butter on Sarah's chin, lied to his mom when he told her that Sarah was into the peanut butter and jam, and Sarah was telling the truth to her mom. However, based on all the evidence, most critical thinkers would believe that Sarah was probably eating the peanut butter and jam.

2. Based on all the evidence in the story, do you think Eddie was into the peanut butter and jam?

(Yes) or No

> Sentence 7 tells us that that Eddie had peanut butter and jam in the corner of his mouth and on the sleeve of his shirt. In sentence 4, Eddie claims he didn't get into the peanut butter and jam, but Sarah did. It is possible that Eddie told his mom the truth in sentence 4, but how would you explain the peanut butter on his mouth? Based on all the evidence, most critical thinkers would decide that Eddie was eating the peanut butter and jam.

Clarissa's Fish

Clarissa just bought a new fish for her aquarium. The fish she bought is one of the four fish pictured below.

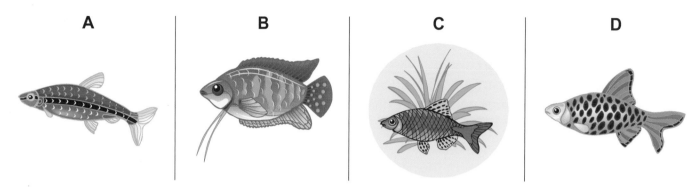

| A | B | C | D |

This is how Clarissa described her new fish:

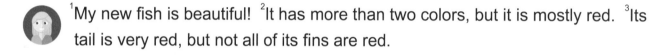

[1]My new fish is beautiful! [2]It has more than two colors, but it is mostly red. [3]Its tail is very red, but not all of its fins are red.

Circle the sentence numbers that support each decision below. Then evaluate all the evidence to find the fish Clarissa bought.

A	B	C	D
This is Clarissa's new fish.	This is Clarissa's new fish.	This is Clarissa's new fish.	This is Clarissa's new fish.
1 2 3	1 2 3	1 2 3	1 2 3
This is not her new fish.	This is not her new fish.	This is not her new fish.	This is not her new fish.
1 2 3	1 2 3	1 2 3	1 2 3

Based on the evidence, which of these fish is Clarissa's fish?
Circle your answer.   A   B   C   D

Eel in the Reef

Three divers were exploring a reef in tropical water when they spotted an eel in the coral. The divers looked at a book about eels and found these pictures of eels.

A	B	C	D

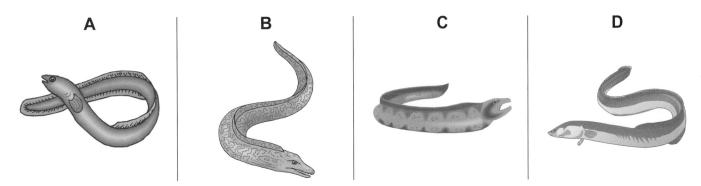

This is how the divers described the eel:

 Diver 1: [1]If you looked deep into its mouth, you could see teeth. [2]The eel was about 3 feet long and looked similar to a snake.

 Diver 2: [3]It looked mean, but didn't act mean. [4]The eel blended in perfectly with the brownish colors of the reef.

 Diver 3:   It was beautiful! [5]It had markings on its body that looked like decorations. [6]It was all different shades of the same color.

Circle the sentence numbers that support each decision below. Then evaluate all the evidence to find the eel the divers saw.

A	B	C	D
This is the eel.	This is the eel.	This is the eel.	This is the eel.
1 2 3	1 2 3	1 2 3	1 2 3
4 5 6	4 5 6	4 5 6	4 5 6
This is not the eel.	This is not the eel.	This is not the eel.	This is not the eel.
1 2 3	1 2 3	1 2 3	1 2 3
4 5 6	4 5 6	4 5 6	4 5 6

Based on the evidence, which of these eels is probably the eel the divers saw? Circle your answer.   A   B   C   D

The Phone Thief

Two witnesses saw a man steal a cell phone out of a car yesterday. The police are convinced the thief is one of these four men.

A	B	C	D
			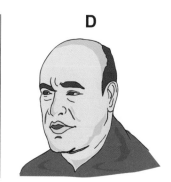

This is how the witnesses described the thief:

 Witness 1: [1]The thief was dressed nice. [2]He was definitely an adult male with dark hair.

 Witness 2: [3]He had a nice shirt on. [4]He didn't have any facial hair. [5]His hair was pretty short. [6]His shirt or jacket was green.

Circle the sentence numbers that support each decision below. Then evaluate the all the evidence to find the person the witnesses described.

A	B	C	D
This is the thief.	This is the thief.	This is the thief.	This is the thief.
1 2 3	1 2 3	1 2 3	1 2 3
4 5 6	4 5 6	4 5 6	4 5 6
This is not the thief.	This is not the thief.	This is not the thief.	This is not the thief.
1 2 3	1 2 3	1 2 3	1 2 3
4 5 6	4 5 6	4 5 6	4 5 6

Which one of these men does the evidence point to?
Circle your answer.

A   B   C   D

The Trash Bandit

Graham heard noises coming from the garbage can in the backyard and walked out to investigate. As he got closer, he heard an animal growl, and then saw it run out of the yard into a large group of bushes.

This is how Graham described the animal:

 [1]It was furry and had pretty short legs and a hairy tail. [2]Its snout was kind of pointed. [3]It looked like its ears were small and kind of rounded. [4]The tail was more than one color and not very long.

A	B	C	D

Circle the sentence numbers that support each decision below. Then evaluate all the evidence to find the animal Graham saw.

A	B	C	D
This is the animal.	This is the animal.	This is the animal.	This is the animal.
1 2	1 2	1 2	1 2
3 4	3 4	3 4	3 4
This is not the animal.	This is not the animal.	This is not the animal.	This is not the animal.
1 2	1 2	1 2	1 2
3 4	3 4	3 4	3 4

Based on the evidence, which of these animals did Graham see?
Circle your answer.

A   B   C   D

5
Evaluating Evidence

After we gather evidence, we need to evaluate it. We evaluate evidence by looking at the evidence for each decision, and then figuring out which decision the evidence suggests. Evaluating evidence is not finding the decision with the most evidence.   Not all evidence is created equal. Some evidence is more important than other evidence. Let's look at a sample problem and try to find the most important evidence.

Example

Look at the recent pictures and read the testimony to try to decide which of the four men below is Bob Baker. Identify the evidence for each face, and then evaluate the evidence to try to make the best decision.

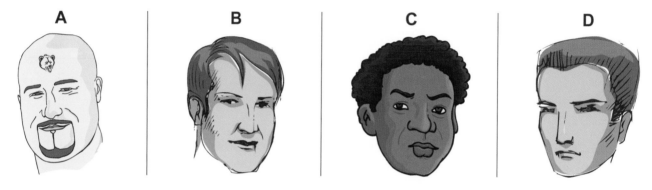

| A | B | C | D |

This is how three acquaintances of Bob Baker described him.

Acquaintance 1: [1]The last time I saw Bob Baker was a little over a year ago. [2]Bob had short brown hair and brown eyes.

Acquaintance 2: [3]I knew Bob Baker when he was just a boy. [4]He had medium length, straight brown hair. He liked to laugh and do crazy things.

Acquaintance 3: [5]I saw Bob Baker a few weeks ago when he just got out of the army. [6]He always wanted attention, so one day he got a crazy tattoo in the middle of his forehead.

Circle the sentence numbers that support each decision below.

A	B	C	D

A

This is
Bob Baker.

1   2   3

4   5   ⑥

This is not
Bob Baker.

1   2   3

4   5   6

B

This is
Bob Baker.

1   ②   3

④   5   6

This is not
Bob Baker.

1   2   3

4   5   ⑥

C

This is
Bob Baker.

1   ②   3

4   5   6

This is not
Bob Baker.

1   2   3

4   5   ⑥

D

This is
Bob Baker.

1   ②   3

4   5   6

This is not
Bob Baker.

1   2   3

4   5   ⑥

1. Which person has the most evidence that he is Bob Baker?   A Ⓑ C D

2. Which sentence has the most important evidence that helped you make your decision?

   <u> 6 </u>

3. Based on the evidence, which of these men is Bob Baker?   Ⓐ B C D

> Even though there is more evidence that person B is Bob Baker, the best evidence points to person A. Only one person has a tattoo in the middle of his forehead. The tattoo evidence is the best evidence because tattoos are permanent (difficult to erase), and the acquaintance saw Bob Baker with the tattoo a few weeks ago. The other acquaintances hadn't seen Bob Baker for over a year before he had a tattoo.

Roberto's Horse

Roberto showed his friends pictures of four different horses. One of the pictures is a picture of his horse.

A	**B**	**C**	**D**
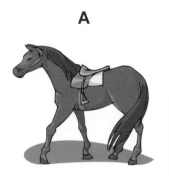	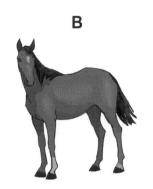	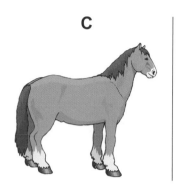	

This is how Roberto describes his horse:

1. My horse is beautiful.
2. Sometimes my horse's legs are wrapped.
3. My horse has some white on one side of his head.
4. My horse has a long tail.
5. My horse is mostly brown with a little white.
6. My horse's body is darker than his tail.

Use the evidence in Roberto's description of his horse to try to find the picture of his horse. Circle the sentence numbers that support each decision below.

A	**B**	**C**	**D**
This is Roberto's horse.	This is Roberto's horse.	This is Roberto's horse.	This is Roberto's horse.
1 2 3	1 2 3	1 2 3	1 2 3
4 5 6	4 5 6	4 5 6	4 5 6
This is not Roberto's horse.	This is not Roberto's horse.	This is not Roberto's horse.	This is not Roberto's horse.
1 2 3	1 2 3	1 2 3	1 2 3
4 5 6	4 5 6	4 5 6	4 5 6

1. Based on the evidence, which of these horses is Roberto's horse?
   Circle your answer.   A   B   C   D

2. What was the most important evidence that helped you identify Roberto's horse?

_____

The Starfish

While walking by a tide pool, Ray and Tammy saw one of the starfish below.

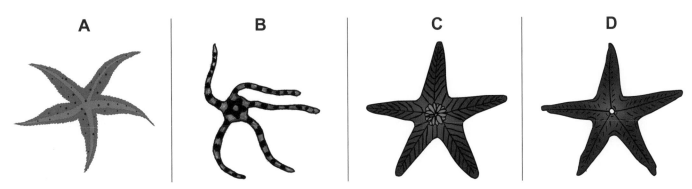

| A | B | C | D |

This how Ray and Tammy described the starfish.

Ray: [1]The starfish had long legs and some black markings. [2]It also had a pretty design in the middle of its body.

Tammy: [3]It was beautiful and looked brightly colored in the water. [4]It had markings that looked like stripes. [5]Its legs were not like other starfish I have seen. [6]This starfish had narrow legs kind of like an underwater spider.

Circle the sentence numbers that support each decision below. Then evaluate all the evidence to find the starfish Ray and Tammy saw.

A	B	C	D
This is the starfish.	This is the starfish.	This is the starfish.	This is the starfish.
1 2 3	1 2 3	1 2 3	1 2 3
4 5 6	4 5 6	4 5 6	4 5 6
This is not the starfish.	This is not the starfish.	This is not the starfish.	This is not the starfish.
1 2 3	1 2 3	1 2 3	1 2 3
4 5 6	4 5 6	4 5 6	4 5 6

Circle your answers.

1. Based on the evidence, which of these starfish did Tammy and Ray see?

    A B C D

2. Which sentence had the most important evidence that led you to your decision?

    1 2 3 4 5 6

The Beetle

Cassie, August, and James found one of the beetles below in their backyard. Use the evidence in their descriptions to find the beetle they saw.

A	B	C	D
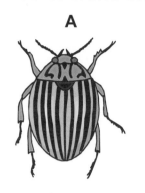	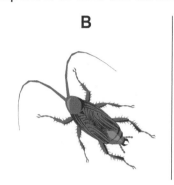		

This is how each of them described the beetle:

 Cassie: ^{1}It had orange on all of its legs. ^{2}It had stripes on the underside of its body.

 August: ^{3}It had stripes. ^{4}It was pretty big compared to most of the bugs we find in the backyard.

 James: ^{5}It was almost as wide as it was long. ^{6}Its orange legs moved slowly as it crawled across my hand.

Circle the sentence numbers that support each decision below. Then evaluate all the evidence to find the beetle Cassie, August, and James saw.

A	B	C	D
This is the beetle.	This is the beetle.	This is the beetle.	This is the beetle.
1 2 3	1 2 3	1 2 3	1 2 3
4 5 6	4 5 6	4 5 6	4 5 6
This is not the beetle.	This is not the beetle.	This is not the beetle.	This is not the beetle.
1 2 3	1 2 3	1 2 3	1 2 3
4 5 6	4 5 6	4 5 6	4 5 6

Circle your answers.

1. Based on the evidence, which beetle did Cassie, August, and James see?

   A   B   C   D

2. Which sentence had the most important evidence that led to your decision?

   1   2   3   4   5   6

Knowledge Is Important!

What you know can help you find and evaluate evidence. For example, if two equally talented critical thinkers are trying to figure out why a car won't start, and one of them knows a lot about how cars work and the other doesn't, the critical thinker who knows a lot about cars is very likely to find the problem before the other critical thinker.

Read the story below and then answer the questions.

Snake Bite!

[1] A year ago we were on vacation on the island of Kauai in Hawaii. [2] My younger brother Brigham and I were hiking along a brushy trail covered with plants and brush when he screamed and said he thought he had just been bitten on the ankle by a snake. [3] He ran up to me crying with a terrified look on his face. [4] I asked him what the snake looked like, but he said he wasn't sure, but it looked green and brown. [5] "Where did it bite you?" I asked. [6] He showed me a scrape on his ankle with one little puncture wound. [7] I looked at it and exclaimed, "Wow! Are you ever lucky!"

[8] He looked up at me and said, "Why am I so lucky, I was just bitten by a snake!"

[9] I then explained to him that the only snakes in Hawaii are tiny little non-venomous snakes that are slightly larger than an earthworm. [10] "Even better news for you is that these tiny snakes don't bite people. [11] My bet is you scraped your ankle on a sharp branch on the side of the path. [12] Can we continue now my brave, young brother?" I asked, smiling down at him. [13] He nodded his head with relief, and then we started hiking again.

Using complete sentences, explain what Brigham's older brother knew that helped him evaluate the evidence differently than Brigham.

_____

_____

_____

Clifford the Cat

[1]Haley and Claire stepped outside of Claire's house to go over to the youth center when they spotted Claire's family cat sniffing a dead bird on the ground. [2]The bird was yellow and green and about 6 inches from head to tail. [3]It was lying close to the glass back door. [4]Claire called to her mom, "Mom, the cat killed a bird."

[5]Haley bent down a few feet from the glass door to look at the dead bird. [6]"Claire, if Clifford killed it, why aren't there any bite marks or blood on the bird?" Haley asked. [7]Haley continued to look for evidence to try and figure out what might have happened.

[8]"Haley, you can't always see bite marks or blood on a bird because of all the feathers. [9]Clifford usually doesn't take a lot of interest in hunting birds, but maybe he was hungry," answered Claire.

[10]Haley stood up for a moment as she continued to think. [11]She finally looked straight at Claire and exclaimed, "I know what happened! [12]Clifford is innocent! [13]Claire, remember the mysterious knock earlier this morning? [14]You went to see who was at the door, but no one was there. [15]I think this bird tried to fly through the glass door and broke his neck when he hit the glass."

[16]"Wow, you are an awesome detective, but how did you figure it out?" asked Claire.

[17]"I was sitting in the living room at our house about a year ago when a bird hit the front window. [18]The impact made quite a noise and I found the bird standing on the ground. [19]He was knocked silly and couldn't fly for a few moments, but eventually was able to fly away. [20]I don't think this bird was so lucky," explained Haley.

Using complete sentences, explain what Haley knew that helped her evaluate the evidence better than Claire.

_____

_____

_____

_____

Expert Knowledge

When we evaluate evidence, we know that some evidence is more important than other evidence. The evidence given to us by an expert is always more important than evidence from someone with limited knowledge of the subject. For example, if you are sick and a friend tells you that it's nothing to worry about, but a medical doctor tells you that you have a serious illness, who would you believe?

You are probably going to believe the medical doctor because the doctor is an expert. Your friend might know something about health and medicine, but unless he is a medical doctor, he probably knows less than the doctor.

Example

Read the story below and then answer the questions on the next page.

The Mushroom

[1]Stuart and his mom Kari were picking blackberries in a field. [2]Kari was a mycologist. [3]Mycologists are scientists who study fungi, such as mushrooms. [4]As Stuart was picking blackberries, he came across some mushrooms. [5]Stuart loved the taste of mushrooms. [6]His mom likes to put them in salads she makes for their family. [7]He also likes the taste of mushrooms on his pizza. [8]Stuart picked a few of the mushrooms and then brought them to his mom so he could show her what he found before taking them home to wash and eat. [9]When his mom saw the mushrooms, her eyes opened wide and she told him, "Never eat any mushroom you find unless you are with an expert who knows it is safe to eat!" [10]Stuart looked at the mushrooms and told her that they looked like the mushrooms that he had seen in one of her salads. [11]His mom took the mushrooms in her hand and told him that many mushrooms look alike, but some mushrooms are deadly poisonous. [12]She then pointed to the mushroom in her hand and exclaimed, "The mushroom in my hand could kill you if you ate it!"

1. Is there evidence in the story that the mushroom could be safe to eat?

   Yes, in sentence 10 Stuart says that he thinks the mushrooms he found look like the mushrooms he has eaten safely before.

2. Is there evidence the mushrooms are not safe to eat?

   Yes, in sentence 12 his mom says that the mushrooms are poisonous and could kill him.

3. Why does the evidence that the mushroom are poisonous outweigh (more important) the evidence that the mushrooms are safe to eat?

   Stuart's mom is a mycologist, and mycologists study fungi such as mushrooms. Stuart's mom's knowledge of fungi helped her evaluate the evidence. Her knowledge of fungi made it possible for her to identify the mushroom in Stuart's hand to know it was poisonous. Knowledge helps our decision making because it helps us find and weigh evidence.

Read the story below and use the evidence to decide if the spider is poisonous.

The Spider Bite

Mai lives in Michigan and was bitten by a spider in her garage. The bite swelled up into a two-inch bump on her arm. She became scared and looked online and found the pictures below of spiders that she thought looked like the spider that had bitten her.

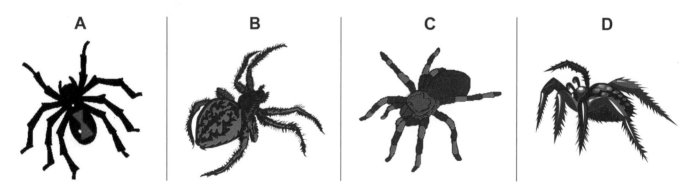

She then went into the house where her parents were visiting with friends. Each of the friends listened to Mai's story and gave their opinion of the spider and the danger.

These are the friends' opinions:

 Adult 1: [1]I heard that there aren't any venomous spiders in Michigan, so the bite is just swollen because you are rubbing it. [2]I was bitten by a spider once on one of my plumbing jobs and it didn't swell, so if you don't rub it, you'll be fine.

Adult 2: [3]I'm a registered nurse and I think you are either having an allergic reaction to the spider bite, or you were bitten by a brown recluse spider. [4]They look like the second spider in your pictures (B). [5]My aunt in Alabama was bitten by a brown recluse spider cleaning her garage, and she told me they were mildly venomous.

Adult 3: [6]I studied spiders when I was in college and only one of the spiders in your pictures lives in Michigan. [7]It is pretty common and venomous, but almost never fatally venomous, so you'll be fine. [8]The spider is called a black widow spider and is the female spider in your pictures with the red hourglass shape on its abdomen. [9]The brown recluse spider is not one of the spiders in your pictures and doesn't live in Michigan.

Circle the sentence numbers that support each decision below. Then evaluate all the evidence to find the spider that bit Mai.

A	**B**	**C**	**D**
This is the spider.	This is the spider.	This is the spider.	This is the spider.
1 2 3	1 2 3	1 2 3	1 2 3
4 5 6	4 5 6	4 5 6	4 5 6
7 8 9	7 8 9	7 8 9	7 8 9
This is not the spider.	This is not the spider.	This is not the spider.	This is not the spider.
1 2 3	1 2 3	1 2 3	1 2 3
4 5 6	4 5 6	4 5 6	4 5 6
7 8 9	7 8 9	7 8 9	7 8 9

1. Using complete sentences, explain which adult provided the best expert knowledge to help identify which spider had bitten Mai.

   _____

   _____

   _____

2. Based on the evidence, which of these spiders most likely bit Mai?
   Circle your answer.   A   B   C   D

Read the story below and use the evidence to decide if the shark is dangerous.

Shark!

[1]My sister and I dropped off the back of the boat into the water with our scuba gear on. [2]It was our first ocean scuba dive. [3]I looked down and saw the coral reef 20 feet below us. [4]It was beautiful with fish of every size and color everywhere. [5]Then the instructor touched our shoulders and pointed to a shark swimming just beyond the reef. [6]The shark was as big as I was! [7]The instructor told us before our dive that we might see a shark, but she also said that most of the sharks she sees around the reef are small and not dangerous. [8]We all stopped to watch the shark. [9]I thought about my older brother's story at dinner last night about a fishing boat that had seen large sharks eating a seal last week. [10]The instructor looked at my sister and me, and then signaled for us to follow her as she continued down to the reef.

1. Identify the evidence for each conclusion.

The shark is dangerous.	The shark is not dangerous.
1 2 3 4 5 6 7 8 9 10	1 2 3 4 5 6 7 8 9 10

2. After identifying and evaluating the evidence, do you think this is a dangerous shark? Circle your answer.   Yes   No

   Use complete sentences to explain your answer.

   _____

   _____

   _____

   _____

   _____

Always Look for New Evidence and Recheck Your Evidence

Police detectives are usually expert critical thinkers. Until they are convinced they have solved a case, they continue to look for new evidence and evaluate the evidence they have to see if it suggests a different conclusion.

Read Part 1 of the story below looking for evidence. Next, answer the questions on the next page to help you decide what to believe.

The Accident
(Part 1)

[1]Two women, one tall and the other short, called the police station to report that they had just watched a car hit a parked car in a parking lot in front of the grocery store. [2]A policewoman drove to the scene and talked to the tall woman and the short woman. [3]Both women told the policewoman that they saw and heard the red car hit the parked blue car in the parking lot. [4]They took the policewoman over to the blue car and pointed to a dent on the car. [5]Next, they took the policewoman over to the parked red car and showed the policewoman a dent on the red car. [6]Finally, they told the policewoman that after the accident, the driver of the red car parked and just walked into the store pretending nothing had happened.

[7]As the policewoman asked the women the time of the accident, the tall woman pointed to a woman coming out of the grocery store and yelled, "That's her! [8]That is the driver that hit the blue car." [9]The driver saw the policewoman motion to her to come join them. [10]This seemed to frighten the driver, but she walked over to them and asked the policewoman how she could help her.

[11]The policewoman asked the driver of the red car if she had hit the blue car before going into the store. [12]The woman became even more nervous, but told the policewoman, "No, I didn't hit any cars today."

[13]"That's a lie," the short woman said, pointing at the nervous driver. [14]The tall woman nodded her head, agreeing with her short friend that the driver was not being truthful.

1. List the evidence that the red car hit the blue car.

_____

_____

_____

_____

2. List the evidence that the red car did not hit the blue car.

_____

_____

3. Based on the evidence in the story, do you think the driver of the red car hit the blue car?

Yes   No

4. Based on the evidence, how sure are you that the driver hit the blue car?

Very Sure   Pretty Sure   Not Very Sure

The Accident
(Part 2)

The policewoman looked at the driver of the red car carefully and asked her if she was sure she didn't hit the blue car. The driver told the policewoman that she was absolutely sure that she didn't hit the blue car.

The policewoman looked at her in disbelief, and then went back to the witnesses and asked them to tell her exactly what they saw and heard. Both witnesses told her that they saw the red car driving by the blue car when they heard a thud. As they turned to see what caused the noise, they saw the red car bouncing like it had hit something. When the driver of the red car didn't stop at the accident and went into the store like nothing had happened, they went to investigate.

When they reached the blue car they saw the dent and then they looked at the red car and saw a dent in it. They then called the police, they said.

The policewoman then asked the witnesses once more to confirm that they both heard and saw the red car hit the blue car. The witnesses told her that they heard the accident, but didn't really see the red car hit the blue car. They just saw the red car shaking after the accident.

The policewoman then went back to the driver of the red car and told her what the witnesses had told her. The driver looked surprised at what the witnesses had told the policewoman and nervously told her that she hit a deep pothole (hole in the road) right behind the blue car which made a loud noise and caused her car to shake, but she never hit the blue car. She then walked with the policewoman behind the blue car and pointed to the hole in the road that she claimed caused the noise that the two witnesses had heard.

Update your evidence lists below to show any new evidence in Part 2 of the story. Next, re-evaluate all the evidence again before answering the questions.

1. List the evidence that the red car hit the blue car.

    _____

    _____

    _____

    _____

2. List the evidence that the red car did not hit the blue car.

    _____

    _____

3. Based on your updated evidence, do you think the driver of the red car hit the blue parked car?

                Yes   No

Looking at the updated lists of evidence, we still have a little more evidence that the red car did hit the blue car, but how would you rate the strength of our evidence?

> The evidence that the red car hit the blue car is still stronger than the evidence it did not, but are you as sure now as you were after Part 1 that the driver of the red car hit the blue car?
>
> Most people would rate the strength of this evidence as strong, but no longer very strong. What makes this evidence strong is that:
> - Two people say they heard the accident and saw the red car shake after the accident.
> - There are dents in both cars.
> - The driver of the red car says she did not hit the blue car and pointed out a hole in the road that she drove over that made her car shake.

Based on the evaluation—the weight and quality of each group of evidence—what conclusion does the evidence support?

> The evidence still supports the witnesses' claim that the red car hit the blue car, but we are a little less certain after learning that the witnesses didn't actually see the accident and learning that there is a hole in the road behind the blue car.

Now read the final part of the story to see if the evidence changes.

The Accident
(Part 3)

The policewoman looked at the hole in the road, but then asked the driver to explain the dents in both cars. The driver said that she couldn't explain the dent in the blue car, but the dent in her car was an old dent from her running into a tree on an icy day last winter. Just then, a woman from the store who had been walking by and heard the policewoman talking to the driver of the red car, stopped and told the policewoman that the store had a video camera that filmed everything that happened in the parking lot. The policewoman and the driver of the red car went into the store and asked to see the video. As they watched the video, it showed the red car already had a dent in it when it entered the parking lot. It also showed the red car made a big bang and shook when it hit the hole in the road before it was parked. Finally, the video showed the red car never hit the blue car.

Update your evidence lists to show the new evidence you learned in Part 3 of the story before evaluating the evidence again.

1. List the evidence that the red car hit the blue car.

_____

_____

_____

_____

2. List the evidence that the red car did not hit the blue car.

_____

_____

_____

_____

3. Based on the evidence in the story, do you think the driver of the red car hit the blue parked car?

                    Yes   No

4. The list of evidence supporting the decision that the red car hit the blue car is longer than the list of evidence that it did not, but what evidence is by far the most important evidence?

_____

_____

5. Based on your evaluation of the latest evidence, use complete sentences to explain why you believe the red car hit or did not hit the blue car.

_____

_____

_____

_____

6
Inferring and Inferences

Inferring is another word for critical thinking. It is using evidence to make a decision. An inference is a decision to believe something after identifying and evaluating the evidence. Here are some examples of how we use the noun inference and the verb infer.

1. Bob heard a deep growl in the bushes and inferred it was a bear.

    Inference: There is a bear in the bushes.
    Evidence: A deep growl came from the bushes.

2. After she made a lot of good saves in soccer practice, Tina made an inference that her coach would use her as a goalie in the next game.

    Inference: Tina's coach will have her play goalie in the next game.
    Evidence: Tina made a lot of good saves in practice.

3. After answering the first six questions correctly, Jim inferred he would do well on the test.

    Inference: He will do well on the test.
    Evidence: Jim answered the first six questions correctly.

4. After hearing me laugh, my sister made an inference that I was the one hiding in the closet.

    Inference: I was the one hiding in the closet.
    Evidence: My sister heard me laugh from the closet.

Inference Practice

Write an inference about each picture and then list the evidence for your inference.

1. Inference   *The coyote just caught and killed the rabbit.*

    Evidence   *The rabbit is dead and the coyote is panting.*

2. Inference _____

   Evidence _____

   _____

3. Inference _____

   Evidence _____

   _____

4. Inference _____

   Evidence _____

   _____

Inference Vocabulary

Use infer, inferred, or inference to complete each sentence.

infer   inferred   inference

1. Tonya _____ she had the flu when she woke up feeling ill, but it turned out that she just had a cold.

2. The laughing he heard coming from inside the house made Jim _____ they were having a party.

3. My _____ that my dog was happy was based on him wagging his tail.

4. Jeff wondered if his sister would _____ he wasn't strong enough to make the hike if he didn't keep up with her.

5. Alone in the backyard, Peyton found a large clump of feathers, so she _____ that her cat had killed another bird.

6. Damie's _____ that her team would win the tourney made us question her evidence.

7. My mom _____ that my dad would miss my soccer game after he called to tell us about his car troubles.

8. The detective made a great _____ that helped us find the thief with the evidence found in his jacket.

9. Based on the lack of evidence, I wasn't able to _____ anything.

10. Karen _____ that the boys were bullying the new boy after she saw the tears on his cheeks.

11. Tom thought Jason's _____ was unsupported by the evidence.

12. I thought Rosaria would _____ that the dog was harmless after watching it play with the other children.

7
Facts and Opinions

Fact

A fact is information that has been proven true. A fact isn't something that could be true; it is something that has been proven true.

Example: Look at the picture below.

Facts About the Picture

- There are two dogs in the picture.

  This fact was proven true by looking at the picture and counting the number of dogs.

- The gray and white dog is bigger than the other dog in the picture.

  This fact was proven true by looking at the picture and measuring the size of each dog.

Write another fact about the picture.

_____

Opinion

An opinion is information that cannot or has not been proven true.

Opinions About the Picture That Cannot be Proven True

- The small dog is the best dog in the world.

  How can anyone prove which dog is the best dog in the world? Is the best dog the smartest dog? Is it the prettiest dog? Is it the most playful dog? How can we prove what the best dog is if we can't agree on what makes a dog "the best dog"?

Opinions About the Picture That Have not Been Proven True

- Someday, these dogs will become friends.

  How do we know if this will turn out true? They might become friends some day, but they might not. We don't know what will happen between these two dogs in the future, so to claim they will someday be friends is an opinion because it has not been proven true.

Write another opinion about the picture.

_____

_____

Here are some more opinions:

- Rhinos will be extinct in five years.

    Rhinos are on the endangered list, but whether they will be extinct in five years, two years, or escape extinction cannot be proven at this point in time.

- Horses are beautiful.

    How could we ever prove that horses are beautiful if we can't all agree on what makes something beautiful?

- I'm the happiest person in the world.

    How could we ever prove who is the happiest person in the world?

Opinions can also be false claims. All of us at some point have claimed something as true, and then found out we were wrong. We thought we were stating a fact, but found out it was really an opinion that wasn't true. Here are some opinions that are false beliefs.

- All dolphins live in the ocean.

    There are freshwater dolphins that live in rivers in Asia and South America. Until they learn about freshwater dolphins, many people might believe that all dolphins live in the ocean. This would be an opinion, but it is a false belief.

- All birds can fly.

    Nearly all birds can fly, but penguins and ostriches are examples of birds that cannot fly.

Practice Problems

Write a fact and an opinion about each picture.

Fact   Opinion

1. _____   _____

   _____   _____

Fact   Opinion

2. _____   _____

   _____   _____

Fact   Opinion

3. _____   _____

   _____   _____

Write a fact and an opinion about each picture.

Fact   Opinion

4. _____   _____

   _____   _____

Fact   Opinion

5. _____   _____

   _____   _____

Fact   Opinion

6. _____   _____

   _____   _____

More Fact and Opinion Practice

Facts are things that have been proven true. Opinions are things that cannot or have not been proven true.

Write "F" for fact and "O" for opinion next to each sentence.

1. _____ Most ducks can swim.

2. _____ Ducks are the coolest birds.

3. _____ Solar is the best heat.

4. _____ Girls are more fun than boys.

5. _____ The sun is larger than Earth.

6. _____ The sun is a star.

7. _____ Most professional basketball players are above average height.

8. _____ Snakes do not have legs.

9. _____ Someone over 6 feet, 8 inches is too tall.

10. _____ I will win next week's race.

11. _____ Mars is farther from the sun than Earth.

12. _____ Some toads live in North America.

13. _____ Some tigers live in Asia.

14. _____ LeBron James is the best basketball player ever.

15. _____ The Mississippi River has more water in it than the Ohio River.

16. _____ The largest sharks live in the ocean.

17. _____ Earth is the most important planet in our solar system.

18. _____ Taylor Swift is the best pop star.

19. _____ Some lions live in Africa.

20. _____ LeBron James played in the NBA in 2014.

21. _____ Part of the Mississippi River runs through Louisiana.

22. _____ Some octopuses have eight legs.

23. _____ Mercury is the prettiest planet in our solar system.

24. _____ Rats make better pets than guinea pigs.

8
Facts and Probable Truths

There are many things that all of us believe to be true that are not facts because they have never been proven true. Believing things that have not been proven true is not a bad thing. We don't have enough time to prove everything we believe to be true, so we often have to accept evidence and conclusions that we believe are probably true.

The important thing to remember about beliefs that are probably true is that they might turn out to be false. Here is an example to think about.

A friend comes to you and tells you that he and his mom saw the girl in the picture below steal something out his mom's car when it was in a store parking lot. Neither of them knew who the girl was, but after they described the girl to the police, the police showed them the picture below and they both said they were positive this was the girl they saw steal from their car. The police confirmed that the girl lived locally and had been arrested before for stealing from cars and homes in the area.

Circle your answers below.

1. The person in the picture stole something out of your friend's car.

            Fact   Probably True   False

2. The police will arrest the girl in the picture.

            Fact   Probably True   False

Based on the evidence in the story and the picture, the answer to both the claims would be probably true. Your friend and his mother identified the girl in the picture as the person they saw steal something from their car. She has been arrested before for similar robberies. Since two witnesses identified the girl in the picture as the thief, the police will likely arrest her again. Even though there is strong evidence that the girl in the picture committed the crime, it hasn't been proven, and so it is not a fact.

Even though the best answers are probably true, both claims were later proven to be false.

The girl in the picture had a sister that looked very similar to her. Her picture is below. After studying the thief's fingerprints found in the car, the police discovered it was the girl's sister dressed in red who committed the crime.

A good critical thinker should know better than to state something is a fact if it is only probably true. A fact has been proven true, but something probably true—no matter how likely you believe it to be true—can turn out to be false.

Fact

A fact is information that has been proven true. A fact isn't something that could be true; it is something that has been proven true.

- Ice is frozen water.

  This has been proven by freezing water into ice and melting ice into water.

- Normal birds have two legs.

  This has been proven by studying birds.

Probable Truth

A probable truth is a belief that we think is true, but has not been proven true, so there is still a chance it could be false.

- In the future, humans will walk on Mars.

  Given we have already landed equipment on Mars, it is likely that at some point in the future, humans will walk on Mars. Although it is likely humans will walk on Mars, it is possible we might not ever walk on Mars. For example, what if Mars was destroyed in the next few years by a giant asteroid?

These ideas might seem unlikely, but if a belief could possibly be false, then it cannot be fact. One of the hardest things we need to do as critical thinkers is separate facts from things that are probably true or probably false. Sometimes it is easy to tell the difference, but sometimes it is very difficult, so let's look at some more examples.

- Computers will become faster in the next five years.

  Computers have become faster nearly every year, and this trend is expected to continue, but it is not guaranteed, so this is probably true. It could turn out to be false.

Look at the picture below.

Facts About the Picture

- Two buildings can be seen in the picture.

  This was proven by counting the number of buildings in the picture.

- There are two people ice skating in the picture.

  This was be proven by counting the ice skaters in the picture.

Probable Truths About the Picture

- The ice is safe for ice skating.

  This is probably true since the people are ice skating, but it is also possible that there is a part of the ice that they haven't skated over that is not safe.

- It will not snow in the next hour.

  This is probably true because snow, like rain, drops from clouds and there are no clouds in the sky in the picture. The cloudless sky suggests it will not snow anytime soon, but it is possible a big set of snow clouds is ready to fill the sky just out of view of the picture.

Practice Problems

Write a fact and something probably true about each picture.

Fact

Probably True

1. __This person is dressed like a__

__football player.__

> This was proven by comparing what the person is wearing with what football players usually wear.

__The boy is going to try to catch__

__the football.__

> This is probably true, but it is possible he tried to catch it and has dropped it. It is also possible that he is throwing it down after scoring a touchdown.

Fact

Probably True

2. _____

_____

_____

_____

Write a fact and something probably true about each picture.

Fact   Probably True

3. _____   _____

_____   _____

Fact   Probably True

4. _____   _____

_____   _____

Fact   Probably True

5. _____   _____

_____   _____

Fact

Probably True

6. _____

_____

_____

_____

Fact

Probably True

7. _____

_____

_____

_____

Fact

Probably True

8. _____

_____

_____

_____

More Fact or Probably True Practice

Classify each statement as Fact or Probably True.

1. My kitten will live longer than the old cat down the street.

    Fact   ⬭Probably True⬭

    Probably, but what if it gets sick or run over by a car.

2. Some cats are scared of dogs.

    Fact   Probably True

3. When she comes home, my mom will be mad about the mess we made.

    Fact   Probably True

4. The pen I used yesterday will not run out of ink today.

    Fact   Probably True

5. In 2013, most summer days were longer than the winter days.

    Fact   Probably True

6. Whales breathe in air by breaking the surface of the water.

    Fact   Probably True

7. Some spider bites can make you sick.

    Fact   Probably True

8. A human will be bitten by a shark next year.

    Fact   Probably True

9. Herbivores are animals that eat plants.

    Fact   Probably True

10. A young wild wolf will hunt with his pack when he grows up.

    Fact   Probably True

9
False and Probably False

Look at the picture above.

False
Something is false if it has been proven false.

- The man looks like he is not moving.

  This has been proven false by looking at the picture and watching how people look when they run.

Probably False
Something is probably false if it is likely false, but might be true.

- The man is running because he is hungry.

  Since it looks like the man is yelling and that he is carrying a bucket of honey and being chased by bees, he is probably running to escape the bees, but it is possible that he is running and the bees are just following him.

The idea that this man is running because he is hungry seems unlikely, but it is possible. So the claim is not false, it is probably false. One of the hardest things we need to do as critical thinkers is separate beliefs that are false from beliefs that are probably false. Sometimes it is easy to tell the difference, but sometimes it is very difficult, so let's look at some more examples on the next page.

False Beliefs or Claims

- Earth does not orbit the sun.

  > Astronomers—scientists who study the universe—have proven this false.

- The Amazon River is not in South America.

  > Geographers—scientists who study the geography—have proven this false.

- Most ducks cannot swim.

  > Ornithologists—scientists who study the birds—have proven this false.

Probably False Beliefs or Claims

- In the next 20 years, human life will no longer exist on Earth.

  > Possible, but very unlikely, so this is probably false.

- Earth will not orbit the sun next year.

  > This could come true, but it would be a major surprise to scientists.

- The Nile River will never flood again.

  > Most scientists would predict the Nile will almost certainly flood again, but it is possible it might not flood again if, for example, the river runs low or out of water after a prolonged drought.

Practice Problems

Write a false claim and a probably false claim about each picture.

False   **Probably False**

1. <u>This person is dressed like a</u>   <u>The person doesn't want to catch</u>

   <u>baseball player.</u>   <u>the football.</u>

> This was proven false by comparing what the person is wearing with what baseball players wear.

> Looking at how the player's hands are positioned, it isn't likely he's not trying to catch the football, but it is possible he doesn't want to catch it. For example, perhaps he is goofing around with his friends.

False   **Probably False**

2. _____   _____

  _____   _____

Write a false claim and a probably false claim about each picture.

False	Probably False

3. _____   _____

   _____   _____

False	Probably False

4. _____   _____

   _____   _____

False	Probably False

5. _____   _____

   _____   _____

False   Probably False

6. _____   _____

   _____   _____

False   Probably False

7. _____   _____

   _____   _____

False   Probably False

8. _____   _____

   _____   _____

10
Fact, Probably True, or Probably False

Look at the picture below and then decide if each claim is fact, probably true, or probably false.

- The frog is mostly green.

  This is a fact since we can see most of the frog in the picture.

- The frog wants to eat the insect.

  This is probably true, but perhaps the frog did eat the insect and decided he didn't like the taste and is spitting it out.

- There is something that looks like an insect in the picture.

  This is a fact as seen in the picture.

- The frog doesn't want to eat the insect.

  This is probably false since frogs often eat insects by snatching them with their tongue. The frog in the picture looks like he is hunting insects, but it could be he is spitting it out.

Practice Problems

Read the story and then mark each statement Fact, PT (probably true), or PF (probably false). Finally, explain why the claim fits the category you chose.

Be careful when trying to decide if something is a fact or probable truth. Remember, a fact is something that has been proven true. Something is probably true or probably false if there is evidence that suggests it, but it is not a fact.

"Here Joey, here Joey," the boy yelled into the neighborhood. A few seconds later, a dog appeared from behind a house and ran to the boy. The boy said "Hey pup, where have you been all day?"

1. __PT__ The boy has been looking for Joey for more than a few hours.

   This is probably true since he asked Joey where he had been "all day,"

   but it is possible the boy hadn't been looking for the dog, but was curious

   where he had been all day.

2. __Fact__ The boy was calling for Joey.

   This is a fact, since it is proven in the story.

3. __PT__ The dog is named Joey.

   This is probably true, but it is possible the boy was looking for his cat,

   Joey, and his dog Rocky ran to him when he heard the boy calling. As the

   dog runs to him, the boy says, "Hey pup, where have you been all day?"

Gatsby Vacation

Mr. and Mrs. Gatsby decided to go on vacation. They packed their car with everything they needed for the trip and began the short drive to a small cabin they rented on a lake in Minnesota.

1. _____ The Gatsbys live in Minnesota.

_____

_____

2. _____ The Gatsbys are driving a red car.

_____

_____

3. _____ The Gatsbys are only planning on going on vacation for one night before returning home.

_____

_____

4. _____ The Gatsbys own a dog.

_____

_____

Read the story and then mark each statement Fact, PT (probably true), or PF (probably false). Finally, explain why the claim fits the category you chose.

Crow's Nest

The beautiful black crow landed on the nest. It was still hungry and tired. It had been a long trip and the crow had flown a long way, but now it was back and could get some rest in its summer home.

1. _____ This is the crow's nest.

_____

_____

2. _____ The crow wanted some food.

_____

_____

3. _____ The crow will live in this area until the end of summer.

_____

_____

4. _____ The crow has never seen this nest before.

_____

_____

Read the story and then mark each statement Fact, PT (probably true), or PF (probably false). Finally, explain why the claim fits the category you chose.

Yard Work

Mr. Lopez agreed to pay Raul $10 each time he mowed the lawn and $10 each time he completely weeded all his gardens. After two weeks, Mr. Lopez paid Raul $30 for the work he agreed to pay in this agreement.

1. _____ Raul earned all the money weeding.

_____

_____

2. _____ Mr. Lopez paid Raul for mowing his lawn or weeding his gardens or both.

_____

_____

3. _____ Most of the money that Mr. Lopez paid Raul was for mowing his lawn.

_____

_____

4. _____ Raul worked for Mr. Lopez after they made their agreement.

_____

_____

11
Venn Diagrams

A Venn diagram is used to show if two or more groups have something in common.

1. Draw a line to show where each of these fish would go in this Venn diagram.

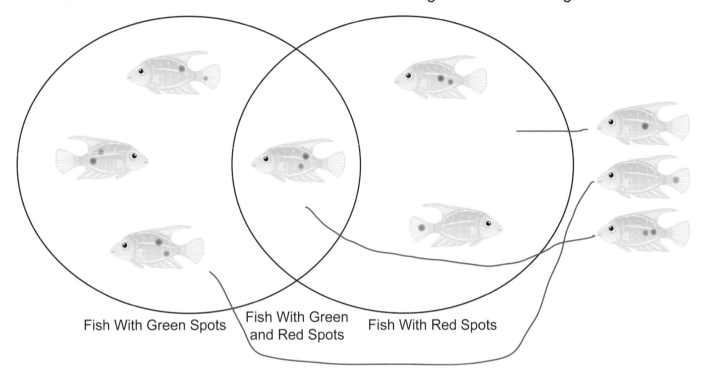

Fish With Green Spots   Fish With Green and Red Spots   Fish With Red Spots

2. Draw a line from each dog below to show where it belongs in this Venn diagram.

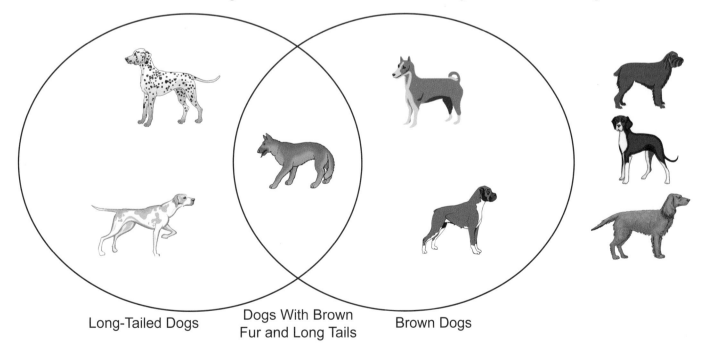

Long-Tailed Dogs   Dogs With Brown Fur and Long Tails   Brown Dogs

3. Label the Venn diagram. Then draw a line from each shape to show where it belongs in the Venn diagram.

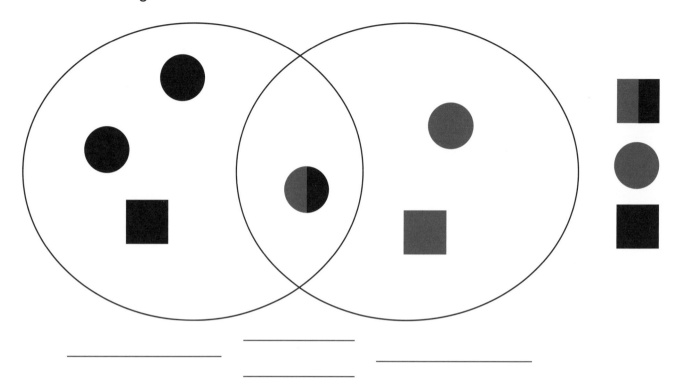

_____   _____
                     _____
                     _____   _____

4. Label the Venn diagram and draw these objects inside it. Each section of the Venn diagram must have one or more objects.

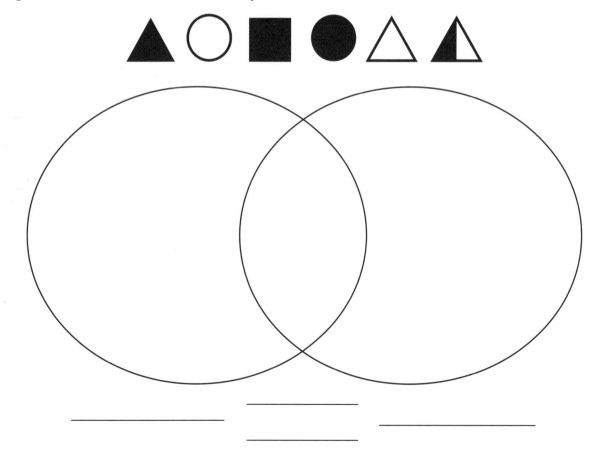

_____   _____
                     _____
                     _____   _____

60

5. Label the Venn diagram and draw all of these objects inside it. Each section of the Venn diagram must have one or more objects.

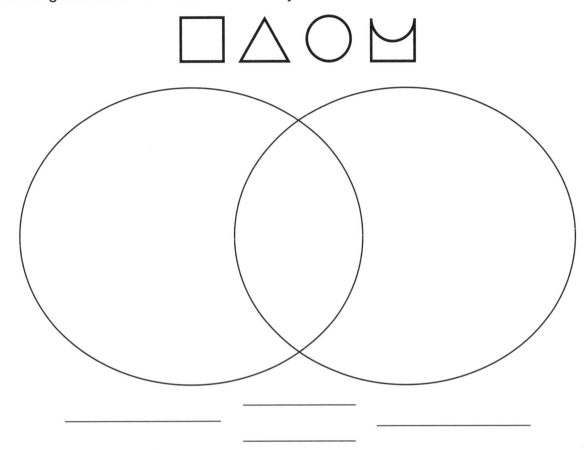

_____

_____   _____

6. Label the Venn diagram. Then draw a line from each face to show where it belongs in the Venn diagram. Each section of the Venn diagram must have one or more faces.

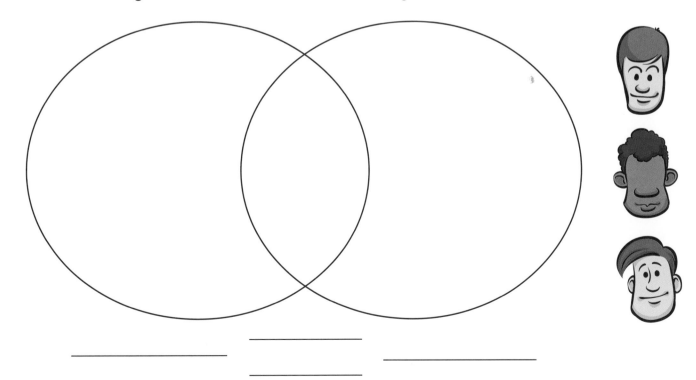

_____

_____   _____

12
Logical Connectives

Logical connectives are words used to connect two or more sentences. "And," "or," and "if" used with "then" are logical connectives.

The Logical Connective "And"

The word "and" is a logical connective that connects two different beliefs. Look at the picture below.

The dog in the picture is brown <u>and</u> named Larry.

The word <u>and</u> connects the claims:

The dog is brown.   <u>and</u>   The dog is named Larry.

Both claims must be true if the sentence is true.

<u>The dog must be brown</u> and <u>the dog must be named Larry</u>.

If dog is brown, but he isn't named Larry, then the sentence isn't true. If the dog in the picture had black hair, but he was named Larry, then the sentence isn't true.

The Cat and the Ball

Look at the picture and mark the sentence T (true) or F (false). Then write each of the claims as separate sentences and mark them T or F.

1. __T__ ___The cat has blue eyes.___

   __T__ ___The cat has black whiskers.___

   __T__ The cat has blue eyes and black whiskers.

2. ____ _____

   ____ _____

   ____ The cat is brown and is next to a green ball.

3. ____ _____

   ____ _____

   ____ The cat has brown eyes and two ears.

4. ____ _____

   ____ _____

   ____ The cat is mostly black and is sitting next to a purple mouse.

The Clown: Part 1

Look at the picture and mark the sentence T (true) or F (false). Then write each of the claims as separate sentences and mark them T or F.

1. ____ _____

     ____ _____

     ____ The clown's nose is purple and the bird is all black.

2. ____ _____

     ____ _____

     ____ The clown is wearing shorts and a colored shirt.

3. ____ _____

     ____ _____

     ____ The clown has a light-colored face and orange hair.

4. ____ _____

     ____ _____

     ____ The clown is wearing colored socks and has a bird in his hands.

The Logical Connective "Or"

The word <u>or</u> is another logical connective that connects two thoughts. The word <u>or</u> in a sentence usually means "one or the other or both."

Today I will eat a banana <u>or</u> an orange for lunch.

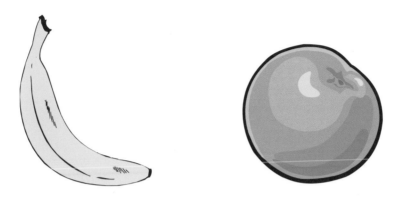

This claim means I will eat a banana <u>or</u> an orange <u>or</u> a banana and an orange for lunch. When <u>or</u> means "one or the other or both," it is called "Inclusive Or."

When <u>or</u> is qualified by the word "either," the meaning changes to "one or the other, but not both."

My mom told me I can eat either pie <u>or</u> cake for desert.

The meaning of <u>or</u> in this sentence is that I can choose to have pie or cake for desert, but I can't choose both. This meaning of <u>or</u> is called "Exclusive Or."

The Clown: Part 2

Look at each picture, read the sentence, and then write in the missing information.

1. __T__ The clown's nose is purple. _____

   __F__ The bird is all black. _____

   __T__ The clown's nose is purple or the bird is all black.

2. ____ _____

   __F__ _____

   __T__ The bird is either his pet or his mom's pet.

3. __F__ _____

   ____ _____

   __T__ The clown uses hairspray or hair gel to make his hair look like that.

4. __T__ _____

   __F__ _____

   ____ The clown acts happy or sad.

Windsurfer Overboard!

Look at each picture, read the sentence, and then write in the missing information.

1. __F__ _____

    __T__ _____

    _____ The surfer either dove in the water or fell off her board.

2. _____ _____

    __T__ _____

    __T__ The surfer is either a male or a female.

3. __F__ _____

    __T__ _____

    _____ The surfer will either sail the board back to shore or paddle it
           back to shore.

4. __T__ _____

    __T__ _____

    _____ The surfer will have fun swimming in the water or fun sailing
           the sailboard.

Lunch Time

Look at each picture, read the sentence, and then write in the missing information.

1. __T__ _____

   __T__ _____

   ____ For lunch today I will have a banana or grapes

2. ____ _____

   ____ _____

   ____ The bananas are left or right of the grapes.

3. ____ _____

   ____ _____

   ____ The bananas are either green or yellow.

4. ____ _____

   ____ _____

   ____ For lunch today I will have either a banana or grapes.

"If – Then" (Conditional) Statements

The words "If" and "Then" are used as logical connectives. Here are some examples of "if – then" used as a logical connective:

If the frog catches the insect, then he will eat it.

If the eagle catches some food, then she will feed it to her chicks.

The two most important things to remember about "if – then" statements are:

1. If both parts of the conditional statement are true, then the claim is true.

<u>Part 1</u> <u>Part 2</u>
If the eagle catches some food, then she will feed it to her chicks. = True
           T   T

2. If the first part of the conditional statement is true and the second part of the conditional statement is false, then the claim is false.

<u>Part 1</u> <u>Part 2</u>
If the lioness catches some food, then she will feed it to her cubs. = False
           T   F

Teaching note: This book does not address logic's treatment of conditional statements where the first part of the conditional statement is false and the second part is true OR both parts of the conditional statement are false. In both instances, logic views these statements as true, but that seems nonsensical in ordinary language.

Conditional Statements Practice

Look at each picture, read each sentence, and then fill in the missing information.

1. __T__   If the snake looks like this, then the snake is a cobra.

   __T__   The snake looks like this.

   _____   The snake is a cobra.

2. __T__   If the leopard is hungry, then the leopard will catch the rabbit.

   __T__   The leopard is hungry.

   _____   The leopard will catch the rabbit.

3. _____   If the animal is green, then it spends much of its time in the water.

   __T__   The animal is green.

   __F__   It spends much of its time in the water.

4. __F__   If it's an eel, then it is poisonous.

   __T__   It is an eel.

   _____   It is poisonous.

Logical Connectives Practice

Use the evidence from the pictures and your knowledge of the logical connectives to write if the sentence is T (true), F (false), or U (unknown).

1. _____ There is a cat in front of the curtain on the left and an elephant behind the curtain.

2. _____ There is a zebra in front of the curtain on the right and an elephant behind the curtain.

3. _____ There are one or more zebras in the picture.

4. _____ If you can see a zebra in the picture, then it is not behind the curtain.

Use the evidence from the pictures and your knowledge of the logical connectives to write if the sentence is T (true), F (false), or U (unknown).

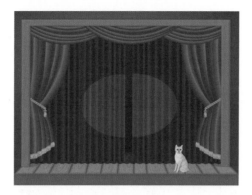

5. _____ If there is a cat in front of a curtain, then there is dog in front of a curtain.

6. _____ There is either a dog behind a curtain or an animal on the left.

7. _____ There is a pig behind the curtain on the left or a zebra in front of one of the curtains.

8. _____ If there is a boat behind a curtain, then there is dog in front of a curtain.

9. _____ If you can see a frog in the picture, then there is another frog in the picture.

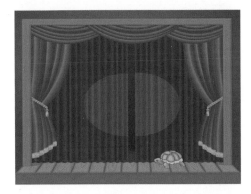

10. _____ There is a turtle in front of a curtain and an eagle in front of the curtain on the right.

11. _____ There is a cat in front of the curtain on the left and an elephant behind a curtain.

12. _____ There is either a snake in front of the curtain on the right or a dog in front of the curtain on the left.

Use the evidence from the pictures and your knowledge of the logical connectives to write if the sentence is T (true), F (false), or U (unknown).

13. _____ There is a pig behind the curtain on the right and a moose behind the curtain on the left.

14. _____ If there is a man in front of a curtain, then he is not behind the curtain.

15. _____ If there is a rhino in front of a curtain, then there is horse in front of a curtain.

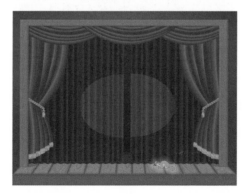

16. _____ There is a weasel in front of a curtain and a cougar behind the curtain on the right.

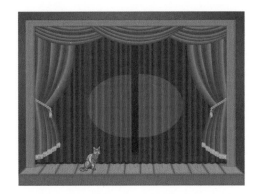

17. _____ There is a goat behind the curtain on the right or a cat in front of one of the curtains.

18. _____ If there is a boar behind a curtain, then there is bird in front of a curtain.

19. _____ If you can see a rabbit in the picture, then there are two more rabbits in the picture.

20. _____ There is either a racoon behind a curtain or an animal in front of the curtain on the left.

13
Advertising

Advertising is used by sellers to try to convince you to buy from them. Advertisements can be found in:

- Websites
- E-mails
- Text messages
- Store windows
- Television

- Signs along roads
- Signs on buildings
- Newspapers
- Magazines
- Radio

By law, an advertiser must be truthful in what they advertise, but many advertisements are written to trick the careless reader into believing the offer is better than it really is. There is an old saying about buying something. The saying is "Buyer beware!" The saying is a reminder to evaluate the evidence for all of the seller's claims.

Always look carefully at the claims in the advertisement. Whatever the ad claims to be true should be listed as claims and whatever conclusion or decision you think is true based on the claims should be used as your conclusion.

Separate the ad's claims from your conclusion by drawing a line in-between the ad claims and your conclusion. Let's look at an example.

Assume everything written in the ad is true.

Suppose you see the ad and conclude that "Their Orange Drink has juice in it."

Step 1: Write down the claims in the ad.

Step 2: Draw a line under the ad claims separating it from your conclusion.

Steps 1 & 2
Example   Our Orange Drink is made with real juice.

Step 3:   Write your conclusion below the ad claims.

> Our Orange Drink is made with real juice.
> _____
> So, the Orange Drink has juice in it.

Step 4:   Evaluate the evidence for your conclusion in the ad claims.

Let's assume that all the advertisement claims in these activities are truthful. How strong is the evidence for this conclusion?

> In this case, there is very strong evidence for the conclusion. If it is true that "the Orange Drink is made with real juice," then it must be true that the drink has real juice in it.

Let's think about another conclusion for the same ad and evaluate how strong the evidence is for this conclusion.

Example 2   Our Orange Drink is made with real juice.
                _____
                So, their Orange Drink is all real juice.

Is the evidence for this conclusion…?

>   Strong   Weak   No Evidence

> There is Weak or No Evidence in the ad (claims) that the Orange Drink is "all" real juice. There is strong evidence that the Orange Drink has some real juice in it, but no evidence that it is all real juice. The Orange Drink could be made with some real orange juice along with other things like water, sugar, and other flavoring.

Look at this last example and decide how strong the evidence is for this conclusion.

Example 3   Our Orange Drink is made with real juice.
                _____
                So, their Orange Drink is made with real orange juice.

Is the evidence for this conclusion…?

>   Strong   Weak   No Evidence

> There is Weak or No Evidence in the ad (claims) that the Orange Drink is made with real orange juice. There is strong evidence that the Orange Drink has some real juice in it, but no evidence that it is real orange juice. The "real juice" could be real apple or grape juice along with artificial orange flavoring.

Practice Problems

The ads below are true. Read each ad and then evaluate how strong the evidence is for the conclusion.

1.   Spend $5 and get a free soda.

   If you spend $5, you get a can of soda.

   Evidence for conclusion: Strong   Weak   No Evidence

2.   Spend $5 and get a free soda.

   If you spend $5, you get your choice of soda.

   Evidence for conclusion: Strong   Weak   No Evidence

3.   Spend $5 and get a free soda.

   If you spend $10, you get two free sodas.

   Evidence for conclusion: Strong   Weak   No Evidence

4.   Buy a candy bar and get another candy bar for free!

So, if I buy a candy bar using this sale, I'll get another candy bar for free.

Evidence for conclusion: Strong   Weak   No Evidence

5.   Buy a candy bar and get another candy bar for free!

So, if I buy any candy bar, I'll get another candy bar free.

Evidence for conclusion: Strong   Weak   No Evidence

6.   Buy any candy bar and get a candy bar of the same type free!

So, if I buy a candy bar, I'll get another candy bar of the same type free.

Evidence for conclusion: Strong   Weak   No Evidence

7.   Buy any candy bar and get a candy bar of the same type free!

So, if I buy two candy bars, I'll get two candy bars fee.

Evidence for conclusion: Strong   Weak   No Evidence

The ads below are true. Read each ad and then evaluate how strong the evidence is for the conclusion.

8.   Our half-price candy sale ends today!

So, all the candy on sale today will be more expensive tomorrow.

Evidence for conclusion: Strong   Weak   No Evidence

9.   Our half-price candy sale ends today!

So, any candy I buy in the store today is half price.

Evidence for conclusion: Strong   Weak   No Evidence

10.   We sell the best candy in the state!

So, they sell candy in the state.

Evidence for conclusion: Strong   Weak   No Evidence

11.

We sell the best candy in the state!

So, they have the best tasting candy in the state.

Evidence for conclusion: Strong   Weak   No Evidence

12.

We have the best prices in the state!

So, they have the lowest prices in the state.

Evidence for conclusion: Strong   Weak   No Evidence

13.

We sell all our candy at low prices!

So, all candy I buy from this seller will be less than candy at most other stores.

Evidence for conclusion: Strong   Weak   No Evidence

The ad below is true. Read the ad and then evaluate how strong the evidence is for each conclusion.

14.   <u>Today's special: Free drink with every hamburger!</u>

So, if you buy two hamburgers, you get two free drinks.

Evidence for conclusion: Strong   Weak   No Evidence

15.   <u>Today's special: Free drink with every hamburger!</u>

So, if you buy one hamburger, you can have a free milk.

Evidence for conclusion: Strong   Weak   No Evidence

16.   <u>Today's special: Free drink with every hamburger!</u>

So, if you buy a hamburger tomorrow, you will not get a free drink.

Evidence for conclusion: Strong   Weak   No Evidence

14
Agreements and Contracts

An agreement is a promise between two or more people. An agreement can be spoken or written. A contract is a written agreement.

When you make a conclusion or decision about an agreement or contract, treat the agreement or contract as claims and then draw a line between the claims and your conclusion or decision.

Even though an agreement is a promise between two or more people, agreements are not always fair, so be careful what you agree to. When evaluating an agreement, remember that any conclusions you make based on the agreement should be supported by evidence in the agreement.

Example

Agreement

On the first day of summer, Tom offered to mow Mrs. Ortega's lawn over the summer any week she decided it needed to be mowed, if she paid him $10 every week over the summer.

Mrs. Ortega agreed to Tom's offer.

If you were to conclude from the agreement that …

Conclusion

If Tom did what he said he would do in the agreement, then Mrs. Ortega should pay Tom $10 at the end of every week over the summer

… then this conclusion can be evaluated drawing a line under the agreement and then writing the conclusion underneath the agreement. It is also helpful to write the word "So" in front of the conclusion. Here is how it should look when you are done:

On the first day of summer, Tom offered to mow Mrs. Ortega's lawn over the summer any week she decided it needed to be mowed if she paid him $10 every week over the summer.
Mrs. Ortega agreed to Tom's offer.

So, if Tom met his responsibility as written in the agreement, Mrs. Ortega should pay Tom $10 at the end of every week over the summer.

Look at the agreement and conclusion and evaluate the evidence in the agreement for the conclusion.

How good is the evidence for this conclusion?

(Strong)   Weak   Little or No Evidence

There is very strong evidence for this conclusion because this is what the agreement says should happen. The conclusion doesn't say that both Tom and Mrs. Ortega kept their word, it just says what Mrs. Ortega should do if Tom followed the agreement. According to the agreement, if Tom did what he was supposed to do, then Mrs. Ortega was supposed to pay him $10 every week over the summer. The agreement doesn't say when in the week Mrs. Ortega was supposed to pay Tom, so the end of the week is okay.

Now evaluate a new conclusion about the agreement between Tom and Mrs. Ortega below.

Conclusion
If Tom doesn't think Mrs. Ortega's lawn needs mowing during the week, then he doesn't need to mow it.

On the first day of summer, Tom offered to mow Mrs. Ortega's lawn over the summer any week she decided it needed to be mowed if she paid him $10 every week over the summer.
Mrs. Ortega agreed to Tom's offer.

So, if Tom doesn't think Mrs. Ortega's lawn needs mowing during the week, then he doesn't need to mow it.

How good is the evidence for this conclusion?

Strong   Weak   (Little or No Evidence)

There is no evidence for this conclusion. The agreement says that Mrs. Ortega gets to decide when the grass needs cutting, so this conclusion is probably false.

Read the agreement and each conclusion and evaluate the evidence in the agreement for the conclusion. Circle an answer and explain your choice.

The Bike Sale

Agreement

Samantha offered to buy Lee's bike for $150 by paying Lee $25 a week for the next 6 weeks. In return for the weekly payments, Lee would let Samantha keep the bike at her house and ride it when and where she wanted. They also had to agree that the bike was in good condition at the time they started the agreement. Both girls accepted the agreement.

Conclusion A

After three weeks, if Samantha can show that the bike is no longer in good condition, then she doesn't have to make any more payments.

How good is the evidence for this conclusion?

Strong   Weak   Little or No Evidence

_____

_____

Conclusion B

Until Samantha makes her final payment, Lee can ride the bike.

How good is the evidence for this conclusion?

Strong   Weak   Little or No Evidence

_____

_____

Read the agreement and each conclusion and evaluate the evidence in the agreement for the conclusion. Circle an answer and explain your choice.

Splitting a Pizza

Agreement

Ramone and Tyler decided to pool their lunch money to buy a pizza and drinks from a nearby snack bar. Tyler volunteered to stand in line, order the pizza, and bring the food they bought to the table while Ramone held their place at the table. If there was any change after paying for lunch, the boys would split it equally. Both boys accepted this agreement.

Conclusion A

If Tyler orders food that he likes and Ramone doesn't like it, then Tyler has to give Ramone his money back.

How good is the evidence for this conclusion?

        Strong   Weak   Little or No Evidence

_____

_____

Conclusion B

If the change from lunch was $5, and Tyler ate 2 pieces of pizza and Ramone ate 3 pieces of pizza, then each boy should get $2.50 in change.

How good is the evidence for this conclusion?

        Strong   Weak   Little or No Evidence

_____

_____

Making Smoothies

Agreement

Richie will make fruit smoothies for Kendra and Deanna for $8 this Saturday afternoon. Richie said his smoothie would have three different types of fruit and would be served in 16 ounce cups. Kendra and Deanna said they would pay for the smoothies once Richie delivered them as promised. Richie, Kendra, and Deanna all accepted the agreement.

Conclusion A

If Richie serves both Kendra and Deanna a fruit smoothie in 16 ounce cups this Saturday afternoon and the smoothies are made with three different types of fruit, then the girls owe him $8.

How good is the evidence for this conclusion?

        Strong   Weak   Little or No Evidence

_____

_____

Conclusion B

If Richie makes the same type of fruit smoothie for Kendra and Deanna on Sunday and they drink them, they owe Richie another $8 for the Sunday smoothies.

How good is the evidence for this conclusion?

        Strong   Weak   Little or No Evidence

_____

_____

15
Common Errors in Reasoning

Emotions and Critical Thinking

Emotions are something that every person has. There are good emotions like love and joy, and bad emotions like hate and jealousy. Emotions are part of what makes us human, but emotions can sometimes interfere with our ability to think clearly.

Learning to spot emotional thinking can help us to see when you or other people are letting negative emotions disrupt their thinking.

Emotional Words Practice

Write the emotional word in each sentence below.

1. She is such an idiot, I can't believe she thinks I'm her friend. ___idiot___

> When someone calls someone an idiot, they are purposely using a hurtful name to describe someone. When you use a hurtful name to describe someone, it is a sign that you have an emotional dislike for that person.

2. I told that big dummy I didn't want to go to the game with him. _____

3. Her face is so ugly that she looks a little like a frog. _____

4. He dropped the ball because he has the brain of a moron! _____

5. She isn't nice, she stinks like old socks! _____

6. Only stupid people like you would believe that. _____

7. The big hippo knows I don't like him. _____

8. I hate her so much, I can't really describe it. _____

Evidence of emotional thinking is not just found in emotional language. Evidence of emotional thinking is often found in a person's behavior. Read the story below and then describe two pieces of evidence that show the older brother's thinking toward his younger brother is clouded with emotion.

[1]Jackson was nearly always pushing his younger brother down for no reason. [2]We asked him to stop it and he did, but then Jackson started telling him to shut up every time he tried to say anything. [3]We thought of him as a friend, but none of us knew Jackson could be so mean.

_____

_____

Practice Problems

Read each story and then look for evidence of emotional thinking to answer the questions.

Lucy   Rico

Carole's Story

[1]My neighbor Linda has had her dog Lucy for four years. [2]She always brings Lucy with her whenever she can. [3]She thinks Lucy is smart because Lucy can do stupid dog tricks. [4]I don't think Lucy is smart, but dumb and ugly. [5]I've seen Lucy run right in front of a car while chasing a ball. [6]Sometimes I think Linda isn't any smarter than her dog. [7]My dog Rico doesn't do any tricks because I never taught him any. [8]I could teach him tricks, but I don't have the time.

1. Which three sentences have emotional language from Carole?

   _____ _____ _____

2. What word in sentence 3 shows that Carole is emotional?

   _____

3. What two words in sentence 4 shows that Carole is thinking emotionally?

   _____   _____

4. What evidence in sentence 6 shows that Carole is thinking emotionally?

   _____

   _____

   _____

Read each story and then look for evidence of emotional thinking to answer the questions.

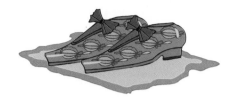

Monica's Story

[1]I think Teresa, the new girl who just moved next door, stole my shoes from our backyard yesterday. [2]I haven't seen them since last night. [3]I think she stole them after I got mad at her and my best friend Lindsey and decided to go inside my house. [4]I just didn't want to be around her fat, ugly face.

[5]I think the only reason that Teresa came over to play with us last night was so she could ruin the friendship between Lindsey and me. [6]Lindsey seems to like her, but I can't wait to tell her that Teresa stole my shoes. [7]I think then she will hate Teresa as much as I hate her.

1. Which two sentences best explain Monica's claim that Teresa stole her shoes?

   _____   _____

2. Is this evidence strong or weak? Circle your answer.   Weak   Strong

3. Which sentence shows that Monica's description of Teresa is full of emotion?   _____

4. Circle the two words below that are most likely emotions that Monica feels toward Teresa.

              love   hate   jealousy   envy

5. What do you think might be the reason that Monica dislikes Teresa?

   _____

   _____

   _____

Damon's Story

[1]I tried out for the soccer team this year and finally made the team. [2]We played our first game today and Kyle scored four of our goals. [3]I could have scored some goals, but everyone always passes to Kyle. [4]If no one passes the ball to me, how can I score? [5]We won the game 5 to 0, but we could have won by more if Kyle wasn't such a ball hog. [6]Everyone congratulated Kyle after the game and treated him like a superstar. [7]Even my best friend Alex just talked about how well Kyle played and didn't even mention how I played. [8]I think Kyle is a dumb jerk who hates to see other people on his team score goals. [9]I've decided not to pass to Kyle in the next game so other people get a chance to score. [10]I don't care if we lose; I want to teach Kyle a lesson!

1. Which sentence has evidence that Kyle is a ball hog?   ____

2. Is this evidence strong or weak? Circle your answer.   Weak   Strong

3. Which three sentences have evidence that Kyle isn't a ball hog? ____ ____ ____

4. What evidence is there that Damon might be jealous of Kyle?   ____ ____ ____

   _____

   _____

5. What two words does Damon use to describe Kyle that best show that his emotions are clouding his thinking?

   _____   _____

6. Explain how Damon's jealousy of Kyle has caused him to make a bad decision about the next soccer game?

   _____

   _____

   _____

Peer Pressure

Peer pressure is when a group of people who are about the same age attempt to pressure (aggressive persuasion) another person their age to do something he or she doesn't want to do.

Practice Problems

Read the story below and look for evidence of peer pressure.

Example

Candy

[1]Roberto, his older brother Marcus, and his sister Julie were asked by their mom and dad to clean up the garage. [2]While cleaning the garage, the children found a box of stored food that had a small, unopened box of candy. [3]Their parents do not let them eat candy without their permission. [4]Julie opened the box and ate one of the candies. [5]Next she offered a piece to Marcus and he ate one of the candies. [6]Finally, she called Roberto over and offered him a candy, but he said he didn't want one. [7]Roberto told his sister he didn't want to get in trouble. [8]Julie and Marcus kept telling Roberto that they ate some of the candy, so he should too. [9]Roberto told them that they would all get in trouble. [10]His brother and sister looked at him, and then told him that if he didn't stop acting like a scared baby they would stop playing with him.

1. Which two sentences have the best evidence of peer pressure?   8   10

> The best evidence of peer pressure is sentences 8 and 10. In sentence 8, Roberto's sister tells him he should eat the candy because they did. In sentence 10, his brother and sister threaten not to play with him if he doesn't eat a piece of candy like they did.

2. Explain why you think Roberto's sister and brother tried to use peer pressure to get Roberto to eat a piece of candy.

> Roberto's older brother and sister probably want Roberto to eat some of the candy they found in the garage so that Roberto is less likely to tell their parents that they ate candy.

Whose Friend Are You?

[1]Kyle was standing in line to buy movie tickets with his best friends, Graham and Augie, when they saw Brigham and Mitch in front of them. [2]Brigham had beaten out Kyle for the starting goalie position on the soccer team, which Kyle had really wanted. [3]When Kyle saw Brigham and Mitch get in front of them, Kyle suggested that the three of them not talk to Brigham. [4]Augie agreed to Kyle's suggestion, but Graham told Kyle he was friends with Brigham, so he didn't want to be mean to him. [5]Kyle and Augie looked at Graham with surprise that he wouldn't go along with the two of them, and then Kyle asked Graham, "Who are your best friends?"

[6]Graham answered, "You two are my best friends."

[7]Kyle then nodded his head at Graham and asked, "So you are going to choose to be friends with Brigham instead of remaining best friends with Augie and me?"

1. Which sentence is an example of a group trying to use peer pressure to get someone to do what they want?

   _____

2. Explain why you think Kyle and Augie tried to use peer pressure to get Graham to be mean to Brigham.

   _____

   _____

Read the story below and look for evidence of peer pressure.

The Brown Slacks

[1]Debbie was in the mall shopping when she ran into a group of girls who lived in her neighborhood. [2]After all the girls said hi, they asked each other what they were shopping for. [3]Debbie told everyone she was shopping for brown slacks, but two of the girls in the other group advised her not to get brown slacks because brown wasn't a pretty color. [4]Debbie didn't agree, so she just told them that she liked brown slacks. [5]The two girls listened, but then one of them asked the other girls in their group if any of them would ever wear brown slacks. [6]All the girls then looked at Debbie with a frown and said they wouldn't even think of wearing them. [7]Then the girl asked Debbie if she was still crazy enough to buy brown slacks.

1. Which two sentences have the best evidence of a group using peer pressure on someone?

   _____ _____

2. Describe an experience you had with peer pressure.

   _____

   _____

   _____

   _____

16
Arguments

What Is an Argument?

An argument isn't always a heated discussion between two people. An argument can also be an attempt to persuade (convince) you that something is true.

Arguments meant to convince you to conclude something is true are made up of claims and a conclusion.

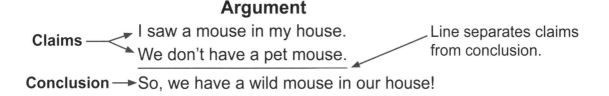

Argument

Claims — I saw a mouse in my house.
We don't have a pet mouse. ——— Line separates claims from conclusion.

Conclusion → So, we have a wild mouse in our house!

Importance of Understanding an Argument's Claims and Conclusion

If someone is trying to convince you to believe something, then it is important to remember that it is their responsibility to make their claims and conclusion understandable. Look at the example below.

Tammy is playing disc catch at the beach with her friend Mai.
Her dog, Lisa, is trying to steal the disc from Tammy and Mai.

So, she won't catch the disc this time.

Who won't catch the disc this time? Which girl is Tammy and which is Mai? Is the conclusion about Tammy, Mai, or Tammy's dog, Lisa? We can't evaluate the argument if we don't fully understand the claim and the conclusion.

If you can't understand the claims or conclusion of someone's argument, then you cannot evaluate their argument. Never accept the conclusion of an argument you don't understand.

Understanding Arguments Practice

Read each argument below. Accept that the claims and conclusion of each argument is true. Then decide if each statement is true, false, or unknown.

Karen and her teammates are playing a soccer match at Coos Bay Middle School. Karen's team has lost only two games in the last two years.

So, they will win the game.

1. Karen plays soccer on the Coos Bay Middle School soccer team.

    True   False   Unknown

2. There is a soccer match being played in Coos Bay.

    True   False   Unknown

3. Karen's team will win the game.

    True   False   Unknown

Trying to Win an Argument by Changing the Argument

Some people try to avoid a tough argument that they don't want to accept as true by changing the argument. There are two common ways to change an argument. One way is to change the argument into a weaker argument called a Straw Man Argument. The other way to change the argument is to change the subject of an argument by creating a Red Herring Argument.

Straw Man Arguments

A Straw Man Argument is when someone tries to change the original argument into a much weaker argument. The new—much weaker—argument can then be proven false. A good way to remember a Straw Man Argument is to remember that it is easy to beat up a straw man. Let's look at a couple of examples.

Jason's argument to Tom:

Original Argument

You picked the last TV show that we watched.

So, I should choose the next TV show we watch.

Tom then changes Jason's argument into a Straw Man Argument by saying Jason's argument is …

Straw Man Argument

Whenever we are watching TV

Jason should always pick what we watch next.

> Tom has produced a Straw Man Argument of Jason's argument because he has turned Jason's argument into an argument that nearly everyone would find unreasonable. Whenever two people are watching TV, why should the same person always get to choose what they watch?

Teaching Note: The three methods taught in this section (Straw Man Arguments, Red Herring Arguments, and Begging the Question) are considered fallacies. Since they are most commonly conscious attempts to win an argument, they are presented here separately from the other fallacies taught in the section on fallacies.

Straw Man Practice

Circle "Yes" if Argument B is a Straw Man Argument and "No" if it is not.

1. Argument A
   If we are on a busy street without a traffic light, then we should not cross the street.
   This is a busy street without a traffic light.

   So, we should not cross the street.

   Argument B
   Whenever we are on a street without a traffic light, then we should not cross the street.
   This is a street without a traffic light.

   So, we should not cross the street.

   Straw Man: Yes   No

2. Argument A
   If a new person moves into our neighborhood, Susan is always mean to the person.
   Teresa just moved into our neighborhood.

   So, Susan will be mean to Teresa.

   Argument B
   Whenever a new person moves to our neighborhood, Susan will be mean to him or her.
   Teresa just moved here from another neighborhood.

   So, Susan is going to be mean to her.

   Straw Man: Yes   No

3. Argument A
   If Nancy is on our spelling team, we will have a good chance to beat all the other teams in the state.
   Nancy is on our spelling team.

   So, we will have a good chance to beat all the other teams in the state.

   Argument B
   If Nancy is on our spelling team, we will never lose to the other teams in the state.
   Nancy is on our spelling team.

   So, we will never lose to the other teams in the state.

   Straw Man: Yes   No

4. Argument A

If you want to successfully complete this book, you will need to work hard.
You successfully completed this book.

So, you worked hard.

Argument B

If I successfully complete this book, I will have to work hard.
I successfully completed this book.

So, I worked hard for nothing.

Straw Man: Yes   No

5. Argument A

If you make meatloaf again for dinner, then I'll become a vegetarian for the night.
You made meatloaf for dinner.

So, I'm a vegetarian tonight.

Argument B

If you make meatloaf again for dinner, then I'm just eating vegetables this evening.
You made meatloaf for tonight's dinner.

So, I'm a vegetarian this evening.

Straw Man: Yes   No

6. Argument A

If you don't start taking care of your pet, then we will find your pet a home where he is cared for.
You don't start taking care of your pet.

So, we will find your pet a home that will give him proper care.

Argument B

If I forget to do something for my pet's care, then you will give my pet away.
I forget to do something for my pet's care.

So, you will give my pet away.

Straw Man: Yes   No

Red Herring Arguments

A Red Herring Argument is when someone tries to avoid an argument by creating another argument with different claims or a different conclusion. A good way to remember a Red Herring Argument is to know where the name came from. A red herring is a fish that was often used to throw hunting dogs off the scent of the animals they were hunting. A person would take a dead red herring and drag it across the trail that the dogs were following, and then the dogs would start following the scent of the red herring instead of the animal they were hunting.

A Red Herring Argument is an attempt to avoid the real argument by changing the argument's claims or conclusion. Here is an example.

Original Argument

Recycling glass will put fewer things in our landfills (dump).
Putting fewer things in landfills saves money and is better for the environment.

So, we should recycle glass.

Red Herring Argument

Only a small amount of recycled plastics can be used to make new plastic products.
Some plastics can't be recycled.

So, recycling isn't a good idea.

> The original argument is about recycling glass. The Red Herring Argument is about recycling plastic. The purpose of this Red Herring Argument is to change the subject from recycling glass to recycling plastics.

Red Herring Practice

Circle "Yes" if Argument B is a Red Herring Argument and "No" if it is not.

1. Argument A
If you dive into water without knowing the depth, you can hit the bottom and injure yourself.
If you dive into water without knowing if there is something between you and the bottom, then you could hit something and injure yourself.

So, never dive into unknown water.

Argument B
Diving into water is one way to get in the water.
If you don't get in the water, you'll never enjoy the water.

So, you need to dive to enjoy the water.

Red Herring: Yes   No

2. Argument A
Many scientific studies have shown that tobacco is bad for your health.

So, you have a better chance of living a healthy life if you don't smoke or chew tobacco.

Argument B
Studies done by scientists show that tobacco is not good for your health.

So, you'll probably live a healthier life if you avoid tobacco.

Red Herring: Yes   No

3. Argument A
Moose are very large animals with big antlers.
Wild moose might look big and slow, but they can actually run fast.
Moose injure and kill many people every year by charging them.

So, you should always avoid getting too close to a moose

Argument B
Moose are very large animals with big antlers.
They are sometimes hunted for food by brown bears and wolves.

So, you should not dress in brown or wear furry clothing around a moose.

Red Herring: Yes   No

4. **Argument A**

Most surfing injuries are not caused by sharks.

Most surfing injuries are caused by unridden surfboards hitting surfers.

So, if you surf, try to avoid unridden surfboards.

Argument B

Some of the most experienced surfers in the world drowned.

More surfers drown each year than are killed by sharks.

So, if you surf, the most important thing is to avoid drowning.

Red Herring: Yes   No

5. **Argument A**

Brown rice has more vitamins and minerals than white rice.

So, you should try to eat brown rice instead of white rice.

Argument B

White rice is tasty, but doesn't have as many vitamins and minerals as brown rice.

So, you should try to replace your white rice with brown rice.

Red Herring: Yes   No

Begging the Question

Some people try to win an argument by putting the conclusion in the claims. When the evidence for an argument's concusion is the conclusion, then the argument is begging the question.

I own the best bike.

So, my bike is the best

The conclusion of the argument is "My bike is the best." The evidence for this conclusion is "I own the best bike," but this isn't evidence, it is just a repeat of the conclusion.

Falcons murder birds to eat them.

So, falcons are murderers.

The conclusion of the argument is "falcons are murderers." There is no evidence that falcons are murderers. The argument's claim "Falcons murder birds to eat them" is just another way of saying "falcons are murderers."

Begging the Question Practice

Circle "Yes" if the argument begs the question and "No" if it does not.

1. If you study hard, you'll get better grades.

   So, study hard and you'll get better grades.

   Does this argument beg the question?   Yes   No

2. Michael yells a lot, so he is irritating.

   So, Michael is irritating because he yells a lot.

   Does this argument beg the question?   Yes   No

3. If my cat wants to play while I'm petting her, she will scratch my hand.

   So, you might get scratched if you pet my cat.

   Does this argument beg the question?   Yes   No

4. Karen is playing better than I am.

   So, she will get more playing time than me in the next game.

   Does this argument beg the question?   Yes   No

5. We should have ice cream every day because it makes every day fun.

   So, we can make every day fun by having ice cream every day.

   Does this argument beg the question?   Yes   No

6. Brownies are the best dessert ever created.

   So, if you want the best dessert, eat a brownie.

   Does this argument beg the question?   Yes   No

17
Valid and Invalid Arguments

Valid Arguments

There are two types of persuasive arguments: 1) Arguments with Valid forms, and 2) Arguments with Invalid forms.

If an argument's form is valid and its claims are true, then its conclusion will always be true.

If an argument of the same form can be created with true claims and a false conclusion, then the argument form is not valid.

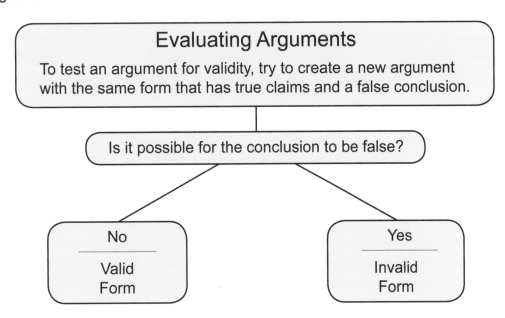

Evaluating Arguments

To test an argument for validity, try to create a new argument with the same form that has true claims and a false conclusion.

Is it possible for the conclusion to be false?

No
___
Valid Form

Yes
___
Invalid Form

Let's practice testing argument forms for validity.

Here is an argument:

If this is my uncle, then he is riding to work.

This is my uncle.
_____
So, he is riding to work.

This is the argument's form:

If   , then   .

So,   .

This is a valid argument form. Remember, a valid argument form is an argument form that will always be true when all its claims are true. In other words, if you see an argument of this form and its claims (1 and 2) are true, then its conclusion must be true.

An argument is not a valid form if you can you create an argument with the same form that has true claims, but a false conclusion.

Since the argument form from the previous page is valid, no matter what you fill into the claims, as long as it's true, then the conclusion will be true. Create a new argument by filling in the claims and conclusion below. Remember, _____ and _____ must be true.

If _____, then _____.
_____
So, _____.

Here is another argument form.

If the animal in the pool is a fish, then the animal can swim.   If ____, then ____.

The animal in the pool can swim.   ____

So, the animal is a fish.   So, ____.

Is this argument form valid? Test to see if the argument form is valid by trying to come up with true claims that produce a false sentence.

If _____, then _____.
_____
So, _____.

Are all animals that can swim fish? A seal swims in water, but it is not a fish, so this is not a valid argument form.

Testing Validity Practice

1. Is this a valid argument form?

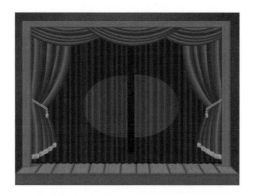

If a normal dog is behind the curtain, then it has four legs.

The animal behind the curtain does not have four legs.
_____
So, it's not a normal dog.

If ____, then ____.

Not ____

So, not ____.

Test to see if the argument form is valid by trying to come up with true claims that produce a false conclusion, and then circle your answer.

If _____, then _____.

Not _____

So, not _____.

Valid Argument Form   Invalid Argument Form

2. Is this a valid argument form?

Boots

All normal cats have tails.

Boots is a cat.

So, Boots has a tail.

All ____ have ____.

____ is a ____.

So, ____ has a ____.

Test to see if the argument form is valid by trying to come up with true claims that produce a false conclusion and then circle your answer.

All _____ have _____.

_____ is a _____.

So, _____ has a _____.

Valid Argument Form   Invalid Argument Form

3. Look at this argument and decide if it is valid.

If this is a healthy bird, then it has healthy eyes.   If ⬤, then ⬤.

If this has healthy eyes, then it can see.   If ⬤, then ⬤.

This is a healthy bird.   ⬤

So, it can see.   So, ⬤.

Is this argument form valid? Test to see if the argument form is valid by trying to come up with true claims that produce a false sentence.

If _____, then _____.

If _____, then _____.

_____

So, _____.

Valid Argument Form   Invalid Argument Form

4. Is this a valid argument form?

All normal hippos have teeth.

The animal behind the curtain has teeth.

So, the animal behind the curtain is a hippo.

All ⬭ have ⬭.

⬭ has ⬭.

So, ⬭ is a ⬭.

Is this argument form valid? Test to see if the argument form is valid by trying to come up with true claims that produce a false sentence.

All _____ have _____.

_____ has _____.

So, _____ is a _____.

Valid Argument Form   Invalid Argument Form

5. Look at this argument and decide if it is valid.

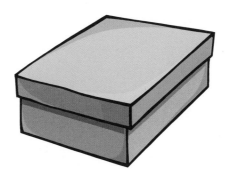

All normal tarantulas have eight eyes.

The spider in the box is a normal tarantula.

So the spider in the box has eight eyes.

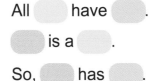

Is this argument form valid? Test to see if the argument form is valid by trying to come up with true claims that produce a false sentence.

All _____ have _____.

_____ is a _____.

So, _____ has _____.

Valid Argument Form   Invalid Argument Form

6. Look at this argument and decide if it is valid.

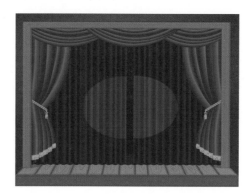

If the animal is a normal whale, then it lives in the ocean.   If ____ , then ____ .

If the animal lives in the ocean, then it lives in saltwater.   If ____ , then ____ .

So, if the animal behind the curtain is a normal whale,   So, if ____ , then ____ .
then it lives in saltwater.

Is this argument form valid? Test to see if the argument form is valid by trying to come up with true claims that produce a false sentence.

If _____ , then _____ .

If _____ , then _____ .

So, if _____ , then _____ .

Valid Argument Form   Invalid Argument Form

7. Look at this argument and decide if it is valid.

All normal birds have two feet.   All ⬭ have ⬭.

The animal behind the curtain has two feet.   ⬭ has ⬭.

So, the animal behind the curtain is a normal bird.   So, ⬭ is a ⬭.

Test to see if the argument form is valid by trying to come up with true claims that produce a false conclusion and then circle your answer.

All _____ have _____.

_____ has _____.

So, _____ is a _____.

        Valid Argument Form   Invalid Argument Form

8. Look at this argument and decide if it is valid.

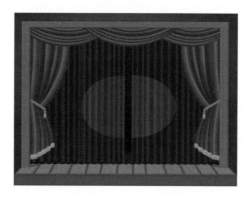

If the animal behind the curtain is a puppy, then it is a dog.   If ____ , then ____ .

It is a puppy.

So, it is a dog.   So, ____ .

Test to see if the argument form is valid by trying to come up with true claims that produce a false conclusion and then circle your answer.

If _____ , then _____ .

_____

So, _____ .

Valid Argument Form   Invalid Argument Form

Invalid Arguments

Most invalid arguments are attempts to convince you that something is true based on the evidence in the argument. Look at the following example.

The beach had shark warnings telling us not to go in the water.

As we looked out at the water in front of the beach, we saw four fins sticking out of the water as large animals swam by about 60 feet from the beach.

So, we saw four sharks swimming off the beach.

The people making this invalid argument are trying to convince us that they saw some sharks swimming off the beach. We know this is an invalid argument because even if the claims are true, the people could have seen dolphins swimming off the beach, not sharks.

Looking at the evidence in the argument, do you believe the conclusion (the people saw sharks)? The best way to decide if you should believe an invalid argument is to evaluate the strength of the evidence.

Evidence that the people saw sharks swimming off the beach:

- They saw a sign warning them not to swim in the water because of sharks.

- They saw four large fins sticking out of the water as four large animals swam off the beach.

> If the people are telling the truth (their claims are true), then they might have seen sharks, but it is possible that they are dolphins, not sharks. Many people who see dolphins in the ocean mistake the dolphins for sharks. Sharks and many species of dolphins have a dorsal fin on their back that sometimes sticks out of the water when they swim near the surface of the water.

Based on the evidence, most of us would judge their evidence as weak. Yes, there was a sign on the beach warning about sharks in the water, but we really have no idea if the fins these people saw were shark fins or dolphin fins.

Let's look at another invalid argument.

I have been to the North Pole many, many times.
Every time I've been to the North Pole, the temperature was freezing cold.

So, it is always freezing cold at the North Pole.

This argument with the same form proves this is an invalid form.

I have been to the desert many, many times.
Every time I've been to the desert, it was never raining.

So, it never rains in the desert.

> It rarely rains in the desert, but it does rain in the desert, so this is not a valid argument form, it is an invalid argument form. Since it is an invalid argument form, we need to evaluate how good the argument's evidence is for the conclusion.

Look at the argument again and then decide the strength of evidence for the arguments' conclusion.

I have been to the North Pole many, many times.
Every time I've been to the North Pole, the temperature was freezing cold.

So, it is always freezing cold at the North Pole.

Evidence for conclusion: Strong   (Weak)   No Evidence

> The evidence for the conclusion is the person's personal experience. We don't know how many times the person visited the North Pole, but to provide strong evidence that the temperature never gets above freezing at the North Pole, the person would have to measure the temperature every day for at least a few years.
>
> As a matter of fact, the temperature at the North Pole is occasionally over the freezing temperature in the month of July, so the argument's conclusion is false.

Let's look at another invalid argument.

How strong is the evidence in this argument for the conclusion?

I like dolphins.

I've read books about dolphins.

Every wild dolphin I've seen or read about lived in an ocean.

So, all wild dolphins live in oceans.

Evidence for conclusion: Strong   Weak   No Evidence

The evidence for the conclusion is that the person has read some books about dolphins and has seen dolphins, but only in the ocean. We don't really know how many books the person has read about dolphins or if the books were science-based books, so most of us would judge the argument's evidence to be weak.

As a matter of fact, there are three species of freshwater dolphins.

Assume you know this doctor and she is telling you the truth.

I've been a medical doctor for 20 years.

The stomach medicine that I tell people to take has always worked.

So, the medicine will work for you.

Evidence for conclusion: Strong   Weak   No Evidence

Since the person making the argument is a medical doctor, the claims are probably true. This person has been a doctor for 20 years, but we don't know how many times she prescribed this medicine to her patients, so some people might argue that the evidence is weak, but most people would judge the evidence strong.

The doctor's knowledge and experience make the evidence for the conclusion strong, so the conclusion is probably true. Probably true is not the same as a fact. It could be that you are the first patient to receive this medicine and not have it work, but this is a strong argument for the conclusion because the claims have strong evidence for the conclusion.

Let's look at one last example. Assume an honest friend told you this:

Last night, an animal knocked over our garbage can to eat some of the garbage.
Last year, my aunt had a raccoon that kept getting into her garbage.

So, a raccoon got into our garbage yesterday.

Since this is a trusted friend, let's assume that the claims are both true. If these claims are true, how strong is the argument's evidence for its conclusion?

Evidence for conclusion: Strong   Weak   No Evidence

Just because your friend's aunt had a raccoon get into her garbage, that isn't strong evidence that the animal that got into your friend's garbage was a raccoon. Raccoons often scavenge, so they commonly go after garbage in the area they live, but so do dogs, bears, and other wild animals. There really isn't much evidence that the animal that got into the garbage was a raccoon except that the person's aunt had a raccoon get into her garbage last year. Where does the person's aunt live? Across the street or across the country? We don't know where she lives and the event happened last year, so most of us would judge this evidence as weak. We don't know what animal got into the person's garbage.

This diagram shows the steps needed to identify and evaluate valid and invalid arguments.

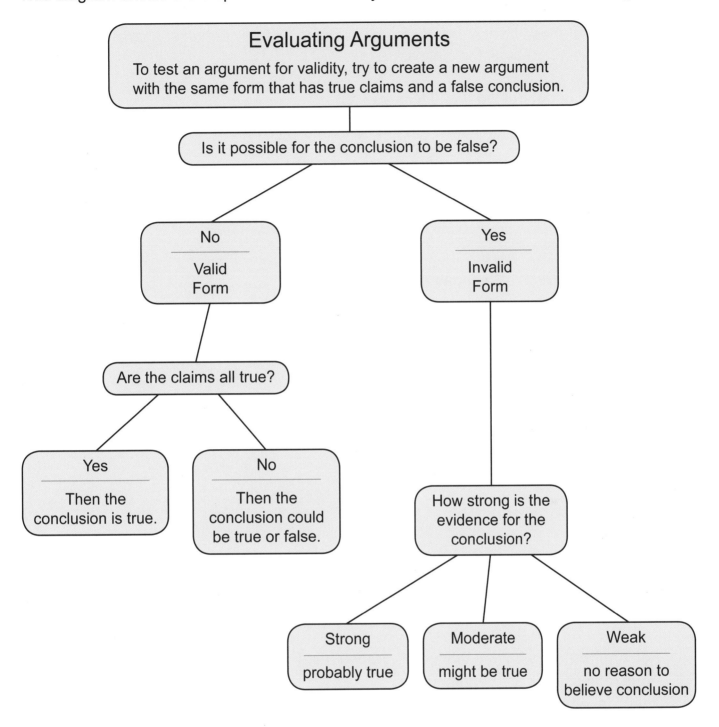

Note that it's possible for both a valid argument with a false claim and an invalid argument to have a true conclusion. Although we can't use these kinds of arguments to prove that the conclusion is true, we should not assume that the conclusion is false.

Evaluating Invalid Arguments Practice

Evaluate each of these invalid arguments by deciding if the evidence supports the conclusion. Assume that all the claims are true.

1. Suppose a good, trusted friend tells you this:

I have used Wilson's Toothpaste for 10 years.
Since I started using Wilson's Toothpaste, I haven't had a cavity.

So, if you use Wilson's Toothpaste, you won't have any cavities.

   Evidence for conclusion: Strong   Weak   No Evidence

2. Suppose an honest friend shows you this picture and then tries to convince you that this is a rattlesnake.

Adult rattlesnakes have a triangular-shaped head.
Adult rattlesnakes are venomous.
This snake has a triangular-shaped head.

So, this is a rattlesnake.

   Evidence for conclusion: Strong   Weak   No Evidence

3. Suppose an honest friend tells you this:

My school textbook that was published last year says that the country of India has more people than the United States.

My mother was born in India and teaches about Indian culture at a U.S. college. She has told me that India has a lot more people than the United States.

So, India has more people than the United States.

Evidence for conclusion: Strong   Weak   No Evidence

4. You and your honest friend Kylie looked at a notice posted in your neighborhood by someone looking for a lost dog. The picture of the dog is below. Kylie called you later all excited claiming that she saw the lost dog run by the front of her house.

The dog I saw was about knee height with four white paws.

He had short brown hair with white hair on his chest and some on his head.

He didn't have a collar.

He had a white spot on his side and a brown tail.

So, I saw the lost dog on the poster.

Evidence for conclusion: Strong   Weak   No Evidence

Evaluate each of these invalid arguments by deciding if the evidence supports the conclusion. Assume that all the claims are true.

5. Suppose an honest friend tells you this:

Jack, one of our neighbor's boys, often asks to borrow my soccer ball.

He loves soccer, but doesn't have a ball of his own.

He usually asks twice a week to borrow my soccer ball.

I went in the house early a few nights ago, and left my soccer ball in my front yard, because it started to storm.

My soccer ball disappeared that night and that was a few days ago.

Jack hasn't asked to borrow my soccer ball since the night it disappeared.

So, Jack stole my soccer ball.

Evidence for conclusion:　　　Strong　　　Weak　　　No Evidence

6. Suppose a good, honest friend tells you this:

When I was visiting an Oregon state park, I saw an eagle.

The park ranger next to me told me it was an eagle.

Oregon has both bald and golden eagles.

This eagle was mostly brown and didn't have a white head or tail.

So, this was a golden eagle.

Evidence for conclusion:　　　Strong　　　Weak　　　No Evidence

7. An honest neighbor feeds your family cat while your family visits relatives who live out of town. Your mom and the neighbor agreed before the family left that the job pays $21 for the week. Your family leaves on Monday the 3rd and returns on Wednesday the 12th. The neighbor feeds the cat while you were gone. The neighbor asks your mom for $27, but your mom only wants to pay him $21.

You agreed to pay me $21 a week to feed your family cat.

$21 dollars a week works out to $3 a day.

You were gone a week and two days.

I fed your cat for a week and 2 days, which is 9 days.

So, you owe me at least $27, not just $21.

Evidence for conclusion: Strong   Weak   No Evidence

8. A caring, honest friend tells you that she prides herself on eating healthy foods and that you should never eat canned soups. She tells you that many of the bestselling canned soups are very high in salt, and it is a fact that eating too much salt can be bad for your health. She introduces you to her grandmother who has never eaten canned soup and is a healthy 91 years old. She suggests that if you follow her advice, you too can live a healthy, long life. You do some checking on the Internet and find out that nutrition experts do recommend that you avoid eating too much salt.

Many of the bestselling canned soups have too much salt.

Eating too much salt is bad for your health according to nutrition experts.

A woman who is healthy and 91 has never eaten canned soup.

So, if you do not eat canned soup, you will live to be 91 or more years old.

Evidence for conclusion: Strong   Weak   No Evidence

9. I think I figured out who the phony salesman is in this story.

Using descriptions from three witnesses, the police arrested a phony salesman who promised to ship people a new cell phone for $10 if they gave him their old phone. The man they arrested is one of four shown.

A	B	C	D

This is what the witnesses told the police.

 Witness 1: [1]The phony salesman seemed honest and caring about getting me a new phone. [2]His hair and mustache looked nice.

 Witness 2: [3]This guy looked nice, but his mustache and hairy eyebrows made me suspicious. [4]I hope the police catch him so I get my phone back.

 Witness 3: [5]He seemed like a nice old man. [6]His face looked kind. [7]His hair was combed straight back. [8]He had a thick mustache and long sideburns.

So, suspect "A" is the phony salesperson.

Circle the sentence numbers that support each decision below.

A	B	C	D
This is the salesman.	This is the salesman.	This is the salesman.	This is the salesman.
1 2 3 4	1 2 3 4	1 2 3 4	1 2 3 4
5 6 7	5 6 7	5 6 7	5 6 7
This is not the salesman.	This is not the salesman.	This is not the salesman.	This is not the salesman.
1 2 3 4	1 2 3 4	1 2 3 4	1 2 3 4
5 6 7	5 6 7	5 6 7	5 6 7

Evidence for conclusion: Strong   Weak   No Evidence

18
Fallacies

A fallacy is an error in reasoning (thinking). A fallacious argument is an invalid argument form that has little or no evidence for the conclusion, so evaluating an argument's evidence for its conclusion is your best protection against fallacious arguments. There are more than 100 recognized fallacies, so trying to learn and memorize all of them is not worth the time.

Let's look at three of the most common fallacies that you will probably recognize.

Hasty Generalization Fallacy

A Hasty Generalization Fallacy is when someone concludes something is true without enough evidence for the conclusion. It usually involves someone observing a few members of a group and then jumping to a conclusion about all the members of the group.

I saw a documentary (true story) movie about a man and a wild brown bear.
The man became friends with the brown bear.
The brown bear never hurt the man.

So, wild brown bears are not dangerous if you are friendly to them.

> Not all brown bears attack every human they meet, but brown bears have attacked humans several times. Just because a brown bear did not attack the man in the film, there is little evidence to conclude that wild brown bears are not dangerous.

Appeal to Ignorance Fallacy

An Appeal to Ignorance Fallacy is when someone concludes something is true because it hasn't been proven false.

I believe Eddy stole Teresa's candy.
No one has any proof that he didn't steal it.

So, Eddy stole Teresa's candy.

If everything we can't prove false is true, then every night when you are sleeping, an evil genius sneaks into your house and turns you into a cat. The evil genius always turns you back into a human and erases your memory of being a cat before you wake up. ☺

Dismissing the Source Fallacy

A Dismissing the Source Fallacy is when someone tries to attack the person or persons making the argument instead of the argument.

My doctor said I have a virus so I should stay away from my friends today.
But you should never take advice from a person that charges money to help people.

So, I'm going to visit my friends today.

What does the fact that a doctor charges money for his or her medical advice have to do with whether staying away from your friends when you are sick is good medical advice? The real question is what evidence did the person offer to support his conclusion (decision) that it is okay to visit his friends when he has a virus? The answer is none. There is no evidence to support his conclusion.

Here's a chart to help you remember these fallacies.

Hasty Generalization	Appeal to Ignorance	Dismissing the Source
When someone concludes something is true about all the members of the group without enough evidence for the conclusion.	When someone concludes something is true because it hasn't been proven false.	When someone tries to attack the person or persons making the argument instead of the argument.

Practice Problems

Read each fallacy and then use the chart on page 126 to identify the type of fallacy.

1. Our neighbor, Mr. Collier, has repaired his dishwasher two times in the last year. Another adult who lives two streets from us repaired his dishwasher last week.

   So, most adults can repair their dishwashers.

   Fallacy _____

2. Susan said that if I knew more about animal care, I would take my cat to the veterinarian.
   I don't think Susan knows what is good for my cat.
   If she was smart, she would have more friends.

   So, my cat doesn't need to see a veterinarian.

   Fallacy _____

3. There is life on the distant, beautiful planet Saturn.
   No one has ever proven that there is no life on Saturn.

   So, there is life on Saturn.

   Fallacy _____

4. Several students from foreign countries come to our town in the summer to work. Some students from Switzerland were caught stealing from a local store.

   So, most students from Switzerland are thieves.

   Fallacy _____

5. I try very, very hard.
   No one has shown me that they try harder.

   So, I try harder than anyone.

   Fallacy _____

6. Anya told me that she likes hanging out with me.
   Anya spends all her time with someone else.

   So, Anya tells lies all the time.

   Fallacy _____

19
Analogy Arguments

Analogy arguments are another type of invalid argument. An analogy argument claims that because two things are similar, what is true of one thing is true of the other. Here is an example.

Sharks are like snakes.
Some snakes are friendly and some are very dangerous.
___
So, always be careful when you are around sharks.

Like all other invalid arguments, the way to evaluate an analogy is to look to see how much evidence the claims have for the conclusion. Just because two things are alike in some ways doesn't mean that they are alike in another way. Here is an example of a bad analogy argument.

Red apples and red potatoes are a lot alike.
Red apples and red potatoes have red skin.
Red apples and red potatoes have a white flesh.
Red apples grow on trees.
___
So, red potatoes grow on trees.

Apples and potatoes are alike in some ways, but they are not alike in many ways. Potatoes are vegetables and apples are fruit. Just because they both look somewhat alike, doesn't mean they grow the same way. Apples grow on trees and potatoes are part of the root of the potato plant.

An analogy argument is an invalid argument. It claims that because two or more things are alike in some or many ways, they should be alike in another way. Be careful! When two or more things are alike in many ways, they are not alike in every way.

A golden eagle and an ostrich are both large.
Both are birds and both have beaks, feathers, and large wings.
Golden eagles can fly.
___
So, ostriches can fly.

Although eagles and ostriches are alike in many way, eagles can fly and ostriches cannot.

Practice Problems

Read each analogy and evaluate the strength of the evidence for the conclusion.

1. Candy is like dessert.
   Desserts are usually made with sugar and so is candy.
   Desserts taste sweet.

   So, candy tastes sweet.

   Evidence for conclusion: Strong   Weak   No Evidence

2. The Parker Grocery store sells the best vegetables and meats in our town.
   The Parker Grocery store is going to start selling candy in their store tomorrow.

   So, the Parker Grocery will sell the best candy in our town starting tomorrow.

   Evidence for conclusion: Strong   Weak   No Evidence

3. Green beans, peas, and broccoli are green vegetables.
   Most people who like the taste of green beans like peas.

   So, they will like the taste of broccoli.

   Evidence for conclusion: Strong   Weak   No Evidence

4. Football, basketball, and baseball are all played with a ball.
   Football players and basketball players are almost never hurt by the ball.

   So, if you play baseball, you are probably not going to get hurt by the ball.

   Evidence for conclusion: Strong   Weak   No Evidence

5. Fruits and vegetables are a lot alike.
   Both fruits and vegetables come from plants.
   Both are full of vitamins and minerals.
   Eating fruits and vegetables is recommended by nutrition experts.
   Parents often tell children to eat their vegetables.

   So, they should also tell children to eat their fruit.

   Evidence for conclusion: Strong   Weak   No Evidence

6. Teachers and babysitters both spend time looking after children.
   Teachers and babysitters are responsible for the children in their care.
   Teachers and babysitters have to deal with good and bad behavior.

   So, teachers and babysitters should be paid the same.

   Evidence for conclusion: Strong   Weak   No Evidence

20
Using Critical Thinking to Make Better Decisions

Now that you know how to use critical thinking to make decisions, it is time to use these skills to improve your own decision making. Fill out a copy of one of the charts on the next two pages to help you make a decision. Here is a list of some practice decisions you could choose if you can't think of your own decision.

1. Should I eat _____ or _____ for lunch today?

2. Should I ask if I can do some work to earn some money?

3. Should I do something nice for my brother or sister this week?

4. Should I volunteer to do some charity work?

5. Should I try out for a sports team?

6. Should I find a good book to read?

7. Should _____ graders have their own cell phones?

8. Should I get paid for all chores I do at home?

9. Is playing computer games good for me?

10. Which is a better pet, a cat or a dog?

11. Is it cruel to keep caged birds as pets?

12. Should I try to play more than one sport or just one?

13. Is ___ hours a night too little, too much, or just enough sleep?

14. Should I invite _____ or _____ or both for my next sleepover?

15. Which is a harder job, _____ or _____?

16. Are big dogs better than small- or medium-sized dogs?

17. Is it more fun to live in the city or the country?

Teaching note: Teachers should also consider 1) Modeling a question to introduce students to using the organizer, and 2) Having students use an organizer with one or more decisions involving a curriculum topic.

What I Need to Decide

_____

_____

_____

Decision 1

_____

_____

_____

Decision 2

_____

_____

_____

Evidence

___ _____

___ _____

___ _____

___ _____

___ _____

___ _____

___ _____

___ _____

Evidence

___ _____

___ _____

___ _____

___ _____

___ _____

___ _____

___ _____

___ _____

☐ **Most Evidence**

☐ **Best Evidence**

☐ **Best Decision**

☐ **Most Evidence**

☐ **Best Evidence**

☐ **Best Decision**

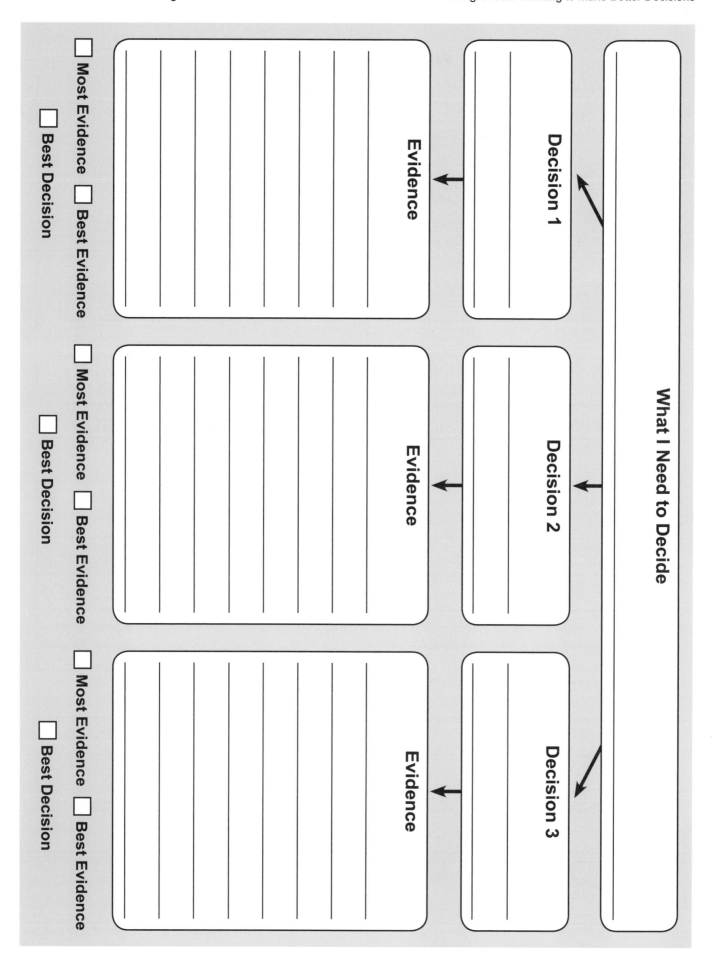

Most Evidence ☐   Best Evidence ☐

Best Decision ☐

Evidence

Decision 1

Most Evidence ☐   Best Evidence ☐

Best Decision ☐

Evidence

Decision 2

What I Need to Decide

Most Evidence ☐   Best Evidence ☐

Best Decision ☐

Evidence

Decision 3

Critical Thinking Posttest

The police are holding these four girls. They are convinced one of these suspects took a purse from a car in a parking lot. The police interviewed three witnesses who saw the thief in the lot.

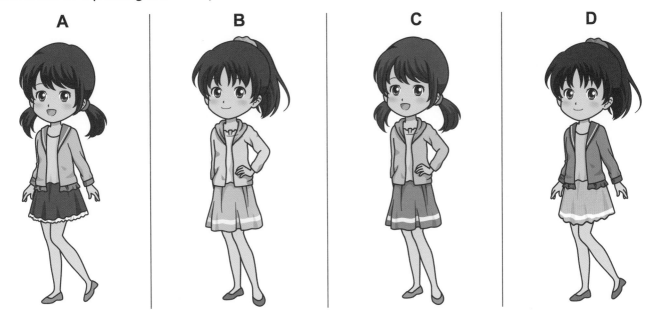

A   **B**   **C**   **D**

Here is how each witness described the thief:

 Witness 1: [1]Her dark hair needed styling very badly. [2]Her shoes went with her outfit.

 Witness 2: [3]She was walking between the parked cars looking inside when she must have seen the purse. [4]She reached in and grabbed the purse and then tried to hide it in her sweater or jacket. [5]I remember that she was wearing something green that looked nice, but it was very different from the color of her skirt. [6]She had her hair tied.

 Witness 3: [7]I remember seeing her brown eyes and a stripe near the bottom of her skirt. [8]Her hair tie did not match her shoes.

Circle the sentence numbers that suggest each suspect is or is not the purse thief. Next evaluate the evidence and then circle your suspect.

A	B	C	D
This is the thief.	This is the thief.	This is the thief.	This is the thief.
1 2 3 4	1 2 3 4	1 2 3 4	1 2 3 4
5 6 7 8	5 6 7 8	5 6 7 8	5 6 7 8
This is not the thief.	This is not the thief.	This is not the thief.	This is not the thief.
1 2 3 4	1 2 3 4	1 2 3 4	1 2 3 4
5 6 7 8	5 6 7 8	5 6 7 8	5 6 7 8

Answers

C is the thief. Sentence 5 eliminates B, who isn't wearing red, sentence 6 eliminates A who has no watch on his visible right hand and sentence 7 eliminates D, whose eyes are hidden by sunglasses so we can't see his eye color. C is wearing a red shirt and light-colored sweater, he has brown eyes, gray slacks, glasses, and brown shoes. We can't confirm from the picture that he is wearing a big watch on his hidden right hand or that he is not wearing a belt, but based on the other evidence it seems likely these statements are also accurate. Though his pants are not as dark as the other suspects, it is important to realize that Witness 1 wasn't comparing him to the other suspects when he gave his description, he was only desribing the one person he saw in the parking lot. Considered in isolation, it is reasonable that Witness 1 would describe C's pants as "kind of dark."

1. What Is Critical Thinking

The Baby Carriage (p. 2)

1. Unknown. Since we can't see in the baby carriage, we don't know if there is anything in it.

2. Unknown. She could be a mom, but she could also be a babysitter, the mom's friend, or someone that sells baby carriages.

3. Unknown. It could be her baby carriage, but it could be a friend's. It could be she has borrowed it from a friend, but it isn't her baby carriage.

Tiger in the Tent (p. 2)

1. Yes. Since there is only one set of tracks, the tracks look like large cat prints, and the tracks lead to a tiger tail sticking out the tent, this is a yes. Another acceptable answer is unknown if you point out that the tiger could have entered from the other side of the tent and the tracks are from another animal in the tent that we can't see.

2. Unknown. We see only the tracks of a single tiger, but perhaps someone entered the tent yesterday and we can no longer see their tracks. Based on the tracks, there is probably just a single tiger in the tent, but we can't be sure. What if there is another entrance to the tent on the other side? We can't be sure if tiger is the only thing in the tent, so the answer is unknown.

3. Yes. The tracks show a single tiger going into the tent and we can still see its tail sticking out of the tent, so the tiger is still in the tent, so this answer is yes.

4. Unknown. The tiger could be hungry, but it could also be curious about what is in the tent, so this is unknown.

The Cort House (p. 3)

1. Mr. Cort. The problem tells us that there are four members of the Cort family and all of the Corts are in the house. Mrs. Cort and two small children can be seen in the house.

2. Three. We only see three sets of footprints and three people in the windows, but we know Mr. Cort is in the house, but not at a window.

3. The other child was probably pulled on the sled. This would match the evidence since there are two sets of adult footprints and only one set of child footprints.

2. Decisions and Conclusions

Practice Problems (p. 5)

Answers will vary. Sample answers:

2. I have decided to avoid the buoy.
   I have concluded that this boat is going over 20 mph.

3. I have decided to take the pass from my teammate.
   I have concluded my teammate wants me to take her pass.

4. I have decided to try a new dive.
   I have concluded I'm going to get wet.

5. I have decided to race this boy down the hill.
   I have concluded the skier is probably going to beat me down the hill.

6. No, a conclusion is a decision you made after thinking about something, so all conclusions are decisions.

3. Beliefs and Claims

Practice Problems (p. 9)

Answers will vary. Sample answers:

	Beliefs	Claims
2.	I believe my mom is listening to me.	This dinosaur was a carnivore.
3.	I believe the bird is scared of the robot.	The robot is scaring the bird.
4.	I believe this is a baby crocodile.	This baby just hatched.

4. Finding Evidence

Clarissa's Fish (p. 14)

C. Sentence 3 eliminates all other choices. B doesn't have a red tail, and A and D don't have any non-red fins. C has a red tail and yellow fins.

Eel in the Reef (p. 15)

C. Sentence 5 eliminates A and D, which don't have any markings, and sentence 4 eliminates B, which isn't brown. C is brown with markings.

The Phone Thief (p. 16)

D. Sentence 2 eliminates A, whose hair isn't dark, and sentence 6 eliminates B and C, who aren't wearing green. D has dark hair and a green shirt.

The Trash Bandit (p. 17)

B. Sentence 1 eliminates A, whose tail is not hairy. Sentence 3 eliminates C, whose ears are not rounded. Sentence 4 eliminates D, whose tail is one color. B has a hairy tail with more than one color and small, rounded ears.

5. Evaluating Evidence

Roberto's Horse (p. 20)

1. D.
2. The evidence that Roberto's horse's body is darker than his horse's tail (sentence 6) was the most important evidence. We learned how important this evidence was when we evaluated it. That evidence is much more important than any other evidence we found.

The Starfish (p. 21)

1. B.
2. The most important evidence is in sentences 5 and 6. The starfish's legs are not like those of most other starfish. A, C, and D all have legs that are typical of starfish. Only B's legs are narrow and spider-like.

The Beetle (p. 22)

1. A.
2. Sentence 5 has the most important evidence. Only beetle A is almost as wide as it is long. The other beetles have narrower bodies.

Snake Bite (p. 23)

Sample answer: Brigham's older brother knew that the only snakes in Hawaii are tiny, non-venomous snakes. These Hawaiian snakes are no larger than an earthworm and do not bite people.

Clifford the Cat (p. 24)

Sample answer: Haley remembered the mysterious knock earlier that morning. She realized that the knock was the sound of the bird hitting the glass door, which caused its death.

The Spider Bite (p. 26)

1. Adult 3 provides the best expert knowledge, having studied spiders in college. Adult 3 is able to identify the spiders from the pictures and knows which one lives in Michigan.
2. A. Spider A matches Adult 3's description in sentence 8.

Shark! (p. 28)

1. Evidence for dangerous: 6, 7, 9
    Sentence 6 tells us the shark is big, which could be evidence that the shark is dangerous. Not all big sharks are dangerous, but big sharks are more likely to be dangerous than small sharks. Sentence 7 tells us that most sharks that visit the reef are not dangerous, but some dangerous sharks visit the reef. Sentence 9 tells us that people on a fishing boat had seen large sharks eating a seal. Sharks that attack and eat seals are considered dangerous, so the large shark by the reef could be one of those sharks.

    Evidence for not dangerous: 7, 10
    Sentence 7 tells us that most sharks that visit the reef are not dangerous so this is evidence that this shark probably isn't dangerous. Sentence 10 tells us that the instructor signaled for the children to follow her down to the reef. This is evidence that the shark is not dangerous.

2. No.
    Some evidence is much more important than other evidence. The instructor saw the shark, watched the shark, and then wanted the children to follow her down to the reef, not stay still or head back to the boat. If the instructor thought the shark was dangerous, she would probably lead them back to the boat or tell them to stay still, not continue down to the reef. This evidence is much more important than the size of the shark or the older brother's story about the fisherman because the dive instructor probably knows which sharks in the area are dangerous and which are not. A critical thinker always weighs all the evidence to determine which pieces of evidence are the most important.

The Accident

Part 1 (p. 29)

1. Evidence that the red car hit the blue car:
    • Tall and short women said that they saw and heard the accident.
    • There was a dent in the red car.
    • There was a dent in the blue car.
    • The driver of the red car looked nervous when the policewoman asked to talk to her.
2. Evidence that the red car did not hit the blue car:
    • Driver of the red car said she did not hit the blue car.
3., 4. Answers will vary.

Part 2 (p. 30)

1. Evidence that he red car hit the blue car:
    • Tall and short women said that they heard the accident and saw the red car shaking after the accident.
    • There was a dent in the red car.
    • There was a dent in the blue car.
    • The driver of the red car looked nervous when the policewoman asked to talk to her.

2. Evidence that the red car did not hit the blue car:
  • The driver of the red car said she did not hit the blue car, but instead ran over a hole in the road behind the blue car which shook her car and made a noise.
  • The policewoman sees a hole in road behind the blue car.

3. Answers will vary.

Part 3 (p. 32)

1. Evidence that the red car hit the blue car:
  • Tall and short women said that they heard the accident and saw the red car shaking after the accident.
  • There was a dent in the red car.
  • There was a dent in the blue car.
  • The driver of the red car looked nervous when the policewoman asked to talk to her.

2. Evidence that the red car did not hit the blue car:
  • The driver of the red car said she did not hit the blue car, but instead ran over a hole in the road behind the blue car which shook her car and made a noise.
  • The policewoman sees hole in road behind the blue car.
  • The driver of the red car said that the dent in her car is an old dent and not caused by hitting the blue car.
  • The video of the parking lot shows the red car had a dent in it when it entered the parking lot and never hit the blue car.

3. Answers will vary.

4. The video in the store is by far the strongest piece of evidence. The store video is a much stronger piece of evidence than any of the other pieces of evidence. This is why a critical thinker should be willing to reevaluate the evidence.

5. Answers will vary.

6. Inferring and Inferences

Inference Practice (p. 35)

Answers will vary. Sample answers:

2. The adult is the child's mother.
   They are dressed similarly and the adult has her hands on the child comforting her like a mother would comfort a child.

3. The lightning set the tree on fire.
   The lightning is striking very close to the tree and lightning strikes often ignites trees.

4. The player in the blue jersey is trying to take the ball from the player in the yellow jersey.
   The player in the blue jersey is grabbing at the player in the yellow jersey and trying to kick the ball.

Inference Vocabulary (p. 36)

1.	inferred	7.	inferred
2.	infer	8.	inference
3.	inference	9.	infer
4.	infer	10.	inferred
5.	inferred	11.	inference
6.	inference	12.	infer

7. Facts and Opinions

Practice Problems (p. 39)

Answers will vary. Sample answers:

	Facts	Opinions
1.	The rider has green pants.	The rider fell off the bike because he was going too fast.
2.	The football has two white stripes.	The player will not catch the football.
3.	There are three people in the canoe.	The older couple are enjoying their vacation.
4.	One duck has a green head.	The green-headed duck is prettier than the other duck.
5.	The man is riding a bicycle.	The man is riding too fast.
6.	The cougar has a tail.	The cougar is acting tough, but it is scared.

More Fact and Opinion Practice (p. 41)

1.	F	13.	F
2.	O	14.	O
3.	O	15.	F
4.	O	16.	F
5.	F	17.	O
6.	F	18.	O
7.	F	19.	F
8.	F	20.	F
9.	O	21.	F
10.	O	22.	F
11.	F	23.	O
12.	F	24.	O

8. Facts and Probable Truths

Practice Problems (p. 45)

Answers will vary. Sample answers:

	Facts	Probably True
2.	There are kittens in the box.	The kittens are playful.
3.	The wolf's fur looks gray.	The wolf is howling to other wolves.
4.	The duck has a green head.	The duck can fly. (Most ducks can fly, and he looks to be taking off or landing, but it is possible that he can't fly.)
5.	The bird looks like it is sitting on eggs.	This is the bird that laid the eggs.

6. The bear has something in its mouth. — The bear is hungry.

7. The bus has wheels. — The bus works.

8. The cat has stripes. — The cat is a tiger cub.

More Fact or Probably True Practice (p. 48)

2. Fact. This has been proven by studying cats.

3. PT. A child probably knows what makes his mom angry, but he could be wrong this time.

4. PT. A working pen is much more likely to run out of ink after today than it is today. Today is one day, but sometime after today (the future) is many days.

5. Fact. Scientists have proven this true using satellite photos and data of Earth.

6. Fact. This has been proven by scientists that study whales.

7. Fact. Scientists who study spiders have proven this true by identifying and testing venomous spiders and their venom.

8. PT. This is almost certain to happen, but it is still possible that it won't.

9. Fact. This has been proven true by studying the meaning of the word in dictionaries.

10. PT. Probably, but only if the young wolf lives long enough to become an adult.

9. False and Probably False

Practice Problems (p. 51)

Answers will vary. Sample answers:

	False	Probably False
2.	The man is wearing a green tie. This was proven false by the picture.	The man does not own the clothes he is wearing. Most people own the clothes they wear, so this is probably false.
3.	There is a dog and cat in the picture. This was proven false by the picture.	One dog is trying to eat the other dog. This is possible, but looking at the picture, it is much more likely that the dogs are playing.
4.	Three birds can be seen in the picture. This was proven false by the picture.	The birds found this nest. This is possible, but most birds build their own nest.
5.	There are two astronauts in this picture. This was proven false by the picture.	The astronaut is looking for a monster. This is possible, but given the concerned look on the astronaut's face, he was probably not expecting a monster.
6.	This is a picture of a cat. This was proven false by the picture.	This owl prefers to hunt in daylight. This is possible, but most owls prefer to hunt at night.

7. This animal is a dog. This was proven false by the picture. — The giraffe is not hungry. This is possible, but it looks like it is trying to eat, so it is probably hungry.

8. This is a lemon. This was proven false by the picture. — The apple isn't ripe. This is possible, but most red apples are ripe.

10. Fact, Probably True, or Probably False

Gatsby Vacation (p. 56)

1. PT. This is probably true, but it is possible it is false. The Gatsby's are driving a short distance to a lake in Minnesota, so they probably live in Minnesota, but perhaps they live close to the Minnesota border and have a short drive to the lake in Minnesota.

2. Fact. This is a fact, they packed their car and the picture shows them driving their packed red car.

3. PF. This is probably false, but it is possibly true. Most people don't call a one night trip a vacation, but it wouldn't be wrong to call it a vacation. It looks like the Gatsbys packed enough suitcases to stay more than one night, but it is possible that they packed extra clothes to make sure they had them in case they needed them.

4. PT. This is probably true, but it is possible it is false. The dog in the car probably belongs to the Gatsbys, but it is possible they are taking care of the dog for a friend.

Crow's Nest (p. 57)

1. PT. This is probably true, but it could be false. The story says she is back and could get some rest in her summer home, so this is probably her nest or the area where she will nest or has a nest (her summer home area). Perhaps this is not her nest, but just the area where she spends her summers. Perhaps she stopped at another bird's nest to see if there was any food.

2. Fact. This is a fact. The story says that she is still hungry.

3. PT. This is probably true, but it could be false. The crow could be killed by a predator or leave just before the end of summer.

4. PF. This is probably false, but it could be true. The story says the crow was back home, so this is probably the crow's nest, but it could just be another nest in her summer area. If the crow knows this area, it has probably seen this nest even if it isn't her nest. It is not likely, but it is possible that this is a new nest in her summer area that she has never seen before.

Yard Work (p. 58)

1. PF. It is possible, but not very likely, that Mr. Lopez needed his gardens weeded three times in two weeks, but didn't need his lawn cut in two weeks.

2. Fact. This has to be true since the money was the result of their agreement and each job in the agreement pays $10.

3. PT. This is probably true because grass usually grows faster than weeds and most people mow their grass more often than they weed their garden, but it is possible that Mr. Lopez had Raul weed his garden twice and mow is lawn once.

4. Fact. This is has to be true because the story says that Mr. Lopez paid Raul $30 for work he agreed to pay in the agreement two weeks after the agreement.

11. Venn Diagrams (p. 59)

2.

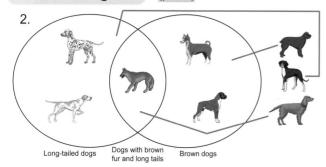

Long-tailed dogs · Dogs with brown fur and long tails · Brown dogs

3.

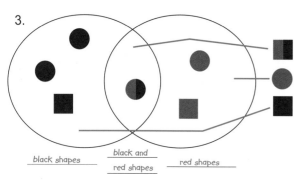

black shapes · black and red shapes · red shapes

4.

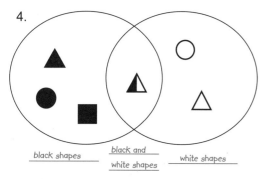

black shapes · black and white shapes · white shapes

5.

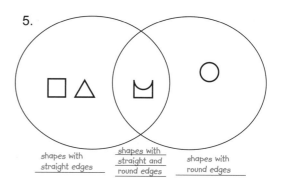

shapes with straight edges · shapes with straight and round edges · shapes with round edges

6.

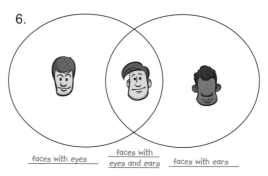

faces with eyes · faces with eyes and ears · faces with ears

12. Logical Connectives

The Cat and the Ball (p. 63)

2. T The cat is brown.
   F The cat is next to a green ball.
   F The cat is brown and is next to a green ball.

3. F The cat has brown eyes.
   T The cat has two ears.
   F The cat has brown eyes and two ears.

4. F The cat is mostly black.
   F The cat is sitting next to a purple mouse.
   F The cat is mostly black and is sitting next to a purple mouse.

The Clown: Part 1 (p. 64)

1. T The clown's nose is purple.
   F The bird is all black.
   F The clown's nose is purple and the bird is all black.

2. F The clown is wearing shorts.
   T The clown is wearing a colored shirt.
   F The clown is wearing shorts and a colored shirt.

3. T The clown has a light-colored face.
   T The clown has orange hair.
   T The clown has a light-colored face and orange hair.

4. T The clown is wearing colored socks.
   T The clown has a bird in his hands.
   T The clown is wearing colored socks and has a bird in his hands.

The Clown: Part 2 (p. 66)

2. T The bird is his pet.
   F The bird is his mom's pet.
   T The bird is either his pet or his mom's pet.

3. F   The clown uses hairspray.
    T   The clown uses hair gel.
    T   The clown uses hairspray or hair gel to make his hair look like that.
4. T   The clown acts happy.
    F   The clown acts sad.
    T   The clown acts happy or sad.

Windsurfer Overboard! (p. 67)

1. F   The surfer dove in.
    T   The surfer fell off her board.
    T   The surfer either dove in the water or fell off her board.
2. F   The surfer is male.
    T   The surfer is female.
    T   The surfer is either male or female.
3. F   The surfer will sail the board back to shore.
    T   The surfer will paddle the board back to shore.
    T   The surfer will either sail the board back to shore or paddle it back to shore.
4. T   The surfer will have fun swimming.
    T   The surfer will have fun sailing the sailboard.
    T   The surfer will have fun swimming in the water of fun sailing the sailboard.

Lunch Time (p. 68)

1. T   For lunch today I will have a banana.
    T   For lunch today I will have grapes.
    T   For lunch today I will have a banana or grapes.
2. T   The bananas are left of the grapes.
    F   The bananas are right of the grapes.
    T   The bananas are left or right of the grapes.
3. F   The bananas are green.
    T   The bananas are yellow.
    T   The bananas are either green or yellow.
4. T   For lunch today I will have a banana.
    T   For lunch today I will have grapes.
    F   For lunch today I will have either a banana or grapes.

Conditional Statements Practice (p. 70)

1. T
2. T
3. F
4. F

Logical Connectives Practice (p. 71)

1. F		11.	F
2. U		12.	F
3. T		13.	U
4. T		14.	T
5. F		15.	F
6. U		16.	U
7. T		17.	T
8. U		18.	U
9. T		19.	T
10. F		20.	U

13. Advertising

Practice Problems (p. 78)

1. Weak or No Evidence for this conclusion. There is strong evidence that after spending $5, you'll get some soda, but no evidence that it will be a can, bottle, or just a poured glass, so the seller (store) will decide.

2. Weak or No Evidence for this conclusion. There is strong evidence that after spending $5, you'll get some soda, but no evidence that you will get your choice of soda, so the seller (store) will decide.

3. Weak or No Evidence for this conclusion. There is strong evidence that if you spend $5, you'll get a free soda, but weak or no evidence that if you spend $5 twice, or $10, you will get two free sodas, so the seller (store) will decide.

4. Strong Evidence. The ad (claims) say that if you buy a candy bar using this sale, you will get another candy bar for free.

5. Weak or No Evidence. There is strong evidence that buying some type of candy bar will get you a second candy bar for free, but little or no evidence that you can buy "any" candy bar and get another candy bar free. The sale could be limited to some candy bars, but not all candy bars.

6. Strong Evidence. The ad states that if you buy a candy bar you'll get another of the same type for free.

7. Strong Evidence. The ad states that if you buy "any" candy bar you'll get another of the same type for free, so the offer is good for any candy bar in the store, so there is strong evidence that if you buy two candy bars, you'll get two more of the same type free.

8. Weak or No Evidence. There is strong evidence that the half-price sale ends today, but the seller can decide to start an even bigger sale tomorrow.

9. Weak or No Evidence. There is strong evidence that there is a half-price sale today, but no evidence if that sale is for "all" the candy in the store. It could be some or all of the candy in the store is on sale, but the ad doesn't tell us.

10. Strong Evidence. The ad says they sell the best candy in the state, so they must sell candy in the state.

11. Weak or No Evidence. There is strong evidence that they sell the "best" candy in the state, but what does it mean to be the best? Is the best candy the best tasting candy, the candy made with the most sugar, the best selling candy, or something else? "The best candy in the state" is a matter of opinion. The ad doesn't tell us what the "best" means, so we don't know.

12. Weak or No Evidence. There is strong evidence that they have the "best prices" in the state, but what does it mean to be the best? Are the best prices the lowest prices, the prices that make the store the most money, or something else? "The best prices in the state" can be a matter of opinion, so we can't be sure what the "best prices" mean in the ad claims.

13. Weak or No Evidence. There is strong evidence that they sell candy at low prices, but what do the ad claims mean by "low prices"? Are low prices the lowest prices in the area, prices that the store thinks are low prices, or something else? "Low prices" can be a matter of opinion and the ad doesn't tell us what is meant by low prices, so we can't be sure.

14. Strong Evidence. The ad claim says you get a free drink with "every" hamburger, so if you get two hamburgers, you will get two drinks.

15. Weak or No Evidence. There is strong evidence you will get a drink, but little or no evidence that the drink will be milk. It could be your choice or the store's choice. The store could choose to give you water.

16. No Evidence. The store is telling you what is today's special, but we don't know from the evidence if the store will have a special tomorrow and if they do have a special tomorrow, what the special will be.

14. Agreements and Contracts

The Bike Sale (p. 85)

A. Little or no evidence. The agreement says that both girls had to agree that the bike was in good condition at the time they started the agreement. There is no evidence that the bike had to remain in good condition throughout the six weeks of payments.

B. Little or no evidence. The agreement says that Samantha could keep the bike at her house and ride it when and where she wanted. Although the agreement will not end until the last (6th) payment has been made, there is nothing in the agreement that says Lee could ride the bike.

Splitting a Pizza (p. 86)

A. Little or no evidence. The agreement says that both Tyler and Ramone agreed that Tyler would order the pizza and drinks and bring it back to the table. There is nothing in the agreement that says what type of pizza Tyler had to order or what would happen if Ramone didn't like the pizza Tyler ordered, so there is no evidence in the agreement that Tyler has to give Ramone his money back if he doesn't like the pizza. The nice thing to do would be to make sure you ordered pizza that both of you enjoyed, but that is not in the agreement.

B. Strong. The agreement says that the boys would split any change equally, so there is strong evidence that if the change was $5, then each boy should get $2.50 each in change.

Making Smoothies (p. 87)

A. Strong. The agreement says that the smoothie "would have three different types of fruit," but it does not say the smoothie will only be made with three different types of fruit, so as long as the smoothie contains three different types of fruit, it was served on Saturday afternoon in 16 oz. cups, then Richie has followed the agreement and the girls owe him $8.

B. Little or no evidence. There is no evidence that Kendra and Deanna agreed to this. They did agree to pay for Saturday smoothies if Richie followed the agreement, but there is no evidence that they agreed to do the same thing on Sunday. You might think they have a moral obligation to pay for the Sunday smoothies, but agreements are not what is moral or right, they are based on what is said or written in the agreement.

15. Common Errors in Reasoning

Emotional Words Practice (p. 88)

2. dummy
3. ugly
4. moron
5. stinks
6. stupid
7. hippo
8. hate

Two pieces of evidence
   Answers will vary. Sample answers:
   1. Jackson was pushing his younger brother down on the ground for no reason.
   2. Jackson began telling his younger brother to shut up every time the younger brother tried to say something.

Carole's Story (p. 89)

1. 3, 4, 6
2. stupid
3. dumb, ugly
4. To suggest that a person (Linda) isn't smarter than a dog is silly and mean (hateful), so it is a sign of Carole's emotional thinking.

Monica's Story (p. 90)

1. 2, 3
   In sentence 2, Monica states the reason she thinks Teresa stole her shoes is she has not seen her shoes since last night. In sentence 3, Monica explains that she believes Teresa stole her shoes after she got mad at her and her best friend, Lindsey, and decided to go in the house.

2. Weak
There are many reasons that could explain the missing shoes besides Teresa stealing them. Monica might have forgot where she left them or someone in her house might have moved them.

3. 4
In sentence 4, Monica uses emotional, mean words when she describes Teresa as having a fat, ugly face.

4. hate, jealousy

5. Answers will vary. Sample answer:
Monica might be jealous of Teresa because Monica's best friend is Lindsey, and Lindsey and Teresa were becoming friends. Monica might feel threatened that Lindsey will spend less time with her if she becomes a good friend of Teresa.

Damon's Story (p. 91)

1. 5
In sentence 5, Damon accuses Kyle of being a ball hog.

2. Weak

3. 3, 6, 7
Sentence 3 tells us that everyone on the team passes the ball to Kyle. If someone is a ball hog, it isn't likely that his teammates would continue to pass to him. Sentence 6 tells us that everyone congratulated Kyle after the game. If Kyle was a ball hog, it isn't likely that everyone would congratulate him after the game. Sentence 7 tells us that even the author's best friend 'Alex' talked about how well Kyle played and apparently didn't complain about Kyle being a ball hog.

4. 8, 9, 10
In sentence 8, Damon calls Kyle a "dumb jerk." This is emotional language. When someone uses emotional language, it is usually evidence that the person's emotions have affected their thinking. Sentence 9 tells us that Kyle doesn't plan to pass to Kyle even if he should. This is more evidence that Damon's emotions are keeping him from thinking clearly. Sentence 10 is evidence that Damon is so jealous of Kyle that he would rather have the team lose than to see Kyle do well.

5. dumb, jerk

6. Damon is so jealous of Kyle getting attention that he is not going to pass the ball to Kyle. This decision is likely to make Damon look bad, not Kyle. Players and coaches will eventually notice what Damon is doing and they will likely be unhappy with Damon.

Whose Friend Are You? (p. 93)

1. 7
Sentence 7 describes Kyle trying to threaten Graham that if he talks to Brigham, he will no longer be friends with he and Augie. This is peer pressure because Kyle and Augie are trying to make Graham do something he doesn't want to do by pressuring him to do what they want or lose their friendship.

2. Kyle is angry or jealous that Brigham beat him out for the goalie position on the soccer team.

The Brown Slacks (p. 94)

1. 5, 6
Sentence 5 describes how one of the girls trying to convince Debbie not to buy the brown slacks tries to get the help of her friends to put more pressure on Debbie. Sentence 6 describes how the other girls help pressure Debbie and how one of the girls even describes Debbie's thinking as "crazy" to add to the pressure.

2. Answers will vary.

16. Arguments

Understanding Arguments Practice (p. 96)

1. Unknown. We know she is playing a match at the Coos Bay Middle School, but she and her teammates could be a visiting team from another school.

2. True. The argument says that Karen and her teammates are playing a soccer match at Coos Bay Middle School. The instructions tell us that the claims and the conclusion are true.

3. Unknown, since it is not clear who "They" refers to. Is "they" Karen's team or the Coos Bay team? Which team does Karen play for? The argument's conclusion is not clear.

Straw Man Practice (p. 98)

1. Yes, Argument B is a Straw Man argument. Argument A claims that busy streets without traffic lights are too dangerous to cross. Argument B claims that you should never cross any street anywhere unless there is a traffic light. If you were on a very quiet street with no cars in sight, but the street didn't have a traffic light, it would be silly to think you should never cross the street.

2. No. Argument B is not a Straw Man argument because it is the same as the original argument. The words are a little different, but it still states that if a new person moves to the neighborhood, then Susan will be mean to her.

3. Yes, Argument B is a Straw Man argument. The arguments have a lot of the same words, but Argument A claims that that with Nancy on the team, the team will "have a good chance" to beat the other spelling teams in the state. Argument B is missing the words "good chance," so Argument B claims that with Nancy on the team, the team will not lose to any of the other teams in the state. Changing the argument from "having a good chance" to "no chance of losing" makes argument different and much weaker than argument A.

4. Yes, Argument B is a Straw Man argument. The arguments have a lot of the same words, but Argument A makes the point that completing this book will require hard work. Argument B changes the conclusion to "work hard for nothing." The words "for nothing" are a big change to the original argument and this change makes the argument stupid or silly.

5. No. Argument B is not a Straw Man argument because Argument B is just a different way of saying Argument A.

6. Yes, Argument B is a Straw Man argument. Argument A claims if the pet owner doesn't start taking care of the pet, then the pet will be given to a home that will give him proper care. Argument B changes the argument to "if you forget to do something for your pet's care—even once—the pet will just be given away to any home."

Red Herring Practice (p. 101)

1. Yes, Argument B is a Red Herring argument. Argument A claims that diving into water without knowing the depth and whether the path is free of obstacles is dangerous, and then concludes you should never dive into unknown water. Argument B has different claims and a different conclusion, so it is an argument with a different subject.

2. No, Argument B is not a Red Herring argument. Argument B is just a different way of making Argument A.

3. Yes, Argument B is a Red Herring argument. Argument A claims that moose can be dangerous animals, so you should keep your distance. Argument B has different claims and a different conclusion, so it is a Red Herring.

4. Yes, Argument B is a Red Herring argument. Argument A claims that most surfers are injured by unridden surfboards, so surfers need to be careful to avoid them. Argument B is about the dangers and drowning while surfing, so it has different claims and a different conclusion.

5. No, Argument B is not a Red Herring argument. Argument B is just a different way of making Argument A.

Begging the Question Practice (p. 104)

1. Yes. This argument begs the question because the conclusion is used as evidence for the conclusion. The argument claims that studying hard will produce better grades and then concludes that studying hard will produce better grades.

2. Yes. This argument begs the question because the conclusion is used in the claims as evidence for the conclusion. The argument claims that Michael is irritating because he yells a lot, and then it concludes that Michael is irritating because he yells a lot.

3. No. This argument does not beg the question because the conclusion is not found in the claims. The argument claims that the owner of a cat has been scratched when trying to pet the cat when the cat wanted to play. The conclusion is a warning to other people that they might get scratched petting the cat, so the conclusion is not found in the claims.

4. No. This argument does not beg the question because the conclusion is not found in the claims. The argument claims that Karen is playing better than he or she is. The conclusion is that this means that Karen will get more playing time in the next game. The claim does not contain the conclusion, so this is not begging the question.

5. Yes. This argument begs the question because the conclusion is used as evidence for the conclusion. The argument claims that ice cream makes every day fun and the conclusion is that we could make every day fun if we had ice cream.

6. Yes. This argument begs the question because the conclusion is used in the claim as evidence for the conclusion. The argument claims that brownies are the best dessert and concludes eating a brownie is eating the best dessert.

17. Valid and Invalid Arguments

Testing Validity Practice (p. 107)

1. Valid. We cannot create an example of this argument form where the claims are true but the conclusion is false, so this is a valid argument form.

2. Valid. We cannot create an example of this argument form where the claims are true but the conclusion is false, so this is a valid argument form.

3. Valid. We cannot create an example of this argument form where the claims are true but the conclusion is false, so this is a valid argument form.

4. Invalid. What if the animal behind the curtain was a cat? Not all animals with teeth are hippos, so this is not a valid argument form.

5. Valid. We cannot create an example of this argument form where the claims are true but the conclusion is false, so this is a valid argument form.

6. Valid. We cannot create an example of this argument form where the claims are true but the conclusion is false, so this is a valid argument form.

7. Invalid. Are all animals with two feet birds? Humans have two feet, but aren't birds.

8. Valid. We cannot create an example of this argument form where the claims are true but the conclusion is false, so this is a valid argument form.

Evaluating Invalid Arguments Practice (p. 120)

1. Weak. If a trusted friend told you this, then the claims are probably true. There is no evidence that the person making the argument is an expert on toothpaste or tooth decay, so the evidence is really the fact that the person has used the toothpaste for 10 years and hasn't had a cavity. Ten years is a long time without a cavity, but has everyone that has used Wilson's toothpaste had the same experience? We don't know, so most of us would judge the evidence as weak.

2. Weak. The claims are all true. Rattlesnakes have triangular-shaped heads, but so do nearly all venomous snakes. All adult rattlesnakes are venomous. Although this argument's claims are true, the claims do not give us strong evidence that this snake must be a rattlesnake.
This snake has a triangular-shaped head, but it is not a rattlesnake. This is a venomous viper snake.

3. Strong. If this is the argument of an honest friend, then the claims are probably true. The evidence of a textbook published last year and his Indian mother's knowledge of India make this strong evidence for the conclusion that India has more people than the United States.
In fact, India has almost four times as many people as the United States. Approximately 1.2 billion people live in India and approximately 300 million people live in the United States.

4. Strong or Weak. Since Kylie is an honest friend, the claims are probably true. Most of us would argue that the evidence that Kylie saw the lost dog is strong since the height, paws, chest hair and head hair all match the description. We cannot see a white spot on the side of the picture, but we can only see one side of the dog. Other people would judge the evidence weak since we cannot verify that the dog in the picture has a white spot on the side we cannot see.

5. Weak. Since the information is from a trusted friend, the claims are probably true. The evidence that Jack stole the soccer ball is:
   1. Jack does not own a soccer ball of his own.
   2. He frequently asked to borrow the soccer ball, but has not asked to borrow the ball since the night the soccer ball disappeared.
The fact that that he has not asked to borrow the soccer ball since it disappeared actually isn't a big surprise if you read carefully. He usually asks to borrow the soccer ball twice a week, so the fact that he hasn't asked to borrow it in a few days might not be surprising. He might ask to borrow the ball today or tomorrow.

6. Weak. There is good evidence that the bird was an eagle, but how good is the evidence that this was a golden eagle? Weak is the best answer, but some might argue that "Strong" is an acceptable answers since this eagle looks more like an adult golden eagle than an adult bald eagle. In fact, this is a young (immature) bald eagle. Young bald eagles are often mistaken for golden eagles. Young bald eagles are mostly brown with some white feathers and they do not grow white heads and tails until they are adults.

7. Strong. The claims are all true based on the story. The conclusion is probably true, but might be false depending on how you see the agreement. Your family was gone more than a week and the neighbor fed the cat for over a week. The weekly rate works out to $3 a day, which would be $27. Unless your mom didn't want the neighbor to feed the cat the last two days your family was on vacation, the neighbor's argument has strong evidence for the conclusion.

8. Weak. There are two problems with the evidence for the conclusion. 1) Just because most bestselling canned soups are high in salt, that doesn't mean that *all* canned soups are high in salt. If eating low-salt foods is important or necessary to living a long, healthy life, then you could eat just the canned soups that are not high in salt. 2) Just because the friend's grandmother is a healthy 91 years old and doesn't eat canned soup, this is very weak evidence for the conclusion that anyone who doesn't eat canned soup will live a healthy, long life to that age. It is possible your friend's grandmother could have eaten canned soup low or high in salt and still lived a long, healthy life. The best evidence that the conclusion might be true is the fact that nutrition experts—who typically base their advice on scientific studies—state that eating too much salt is bad for your health.

9. Weak. There is some evidence that suspect A was the thief, but better evidence that suspect D was the thief. Suspect A didn't have a thick mustache. Suspect B and C didn't have long sideburns or comb their hair straight back. Suspect D had a thick mustache, combed his hair straight back, and had long sideburns, so there is weak evidence for suspect A and strong evidence for suspect D.

18. Fallacies
Practice Problems (p. 127)

1. Hasty Generalization. The fact that two adults in a neighborhood repaired their dishwashers isn't very strong evidence that "most" adults can repair their dishwashers. Depending on the size of the neighborhood, two adults might be a very small number of the total number of adults in the neighborhood—and an even smaller number of all adults.

2. Dismissing the Source. This argument is not evaluating Susan's evidence for her conclusion; she is attacking Susan by claiming she has more friends than Susan. How many friends Susan has does not have anything to do with Susan's conclusion or her evidence for the conclusion.

3. Appeal to Ignorance. Scientists have no reason to believe there is life on the planet. There might be life on Saturn, but right now there is little or no evidence of it. The fact that no one has proven there isn't life on Saturn is not strong evidence that there is life on Saturn.

4. Hasty Generalization. The fact that some Swiss students were caught stealing is not strong evidence that "most" Swiss students steal (are thieves). The group of Swiss students is a very small part of the much larger group of Swiss students.

5. Appeal to Ignorance. The fact that no one has shown (proven) to this person that they try as hard or harder than this person is not strong evidence that they try the hardest. They might try hard, but they have provided little or no evidence that they try the hardest.

6. Hasty Generalization. Anya was either telling the truth or being dishonest when she told this person that she likes hanging out with them. Even if she was lying, this by itself is moderate or weak evidence that she lies "all the time."

19. Analogy Arguments
Practice Problems (p. 129)

1. Strong. This is a good analogy argument and it is true.

2. Weak. The Parker Grocery probably sells many things besides vegetables and meats, so the fact that they sell the best vegetables and meats is not strong evidence that they will sell the best candy in town.

3. Weak. There are a lot of green vegetables. Just because someone likes the taste of two green vegetables it is not strong evidence that they will like the taste of another green vegetable (e.g. broccoli).

4. Weak. There are a lot of sports played with balls. Just because two of those sports use a ball that almost never injures a player, that is weak evidence that the other sports that use a ball are just as unlikely to have players injured by the ball.

5. Strong. There is strong evidence that both are healthy food groups for humans. So there is strong evidence for the conclusion.

6. Weak. Just because teachers and babysitters have three things in common isn't much evidence that they should be paid the same. Teachers teach, but most babysitters do not. Babysitters are often teenagers, but teachers are usually adults.

Posttest (p. 133)

B is the thief. Sentence 5 eliminates D, who is wearing a green skirt and thus not wearing anything green that is very different from her skirt. Sentence 8 eliminates A and C, whose hair ties match their shoes. B is wearing a green jacket (that is different from the color of her skirt), she has her hair tied, she has brown eyes and a stripe near the bottom of her skirt, and her hair tie does not match her shoes.

PRACTICAL CRITICAL THINKING

Practical Critical Thinking engages students in the study of critical thinking. It lays a strong foundation in the important cognitive skills necessary for critical thinking, such as comprehension, analysis, evaluation, construction, creativity, and communication. Through fun and concrete activities—including Thought Experiments, Student Polls, Practice Sessions, Games and Puzzles, Predictions, and Important Takeaways—students explore topics essential to critical thinking, filling their Critical Thinking Tool Box with tools that will help them as critical thinkers, and applying critical thinking directly to their own lives. Additional individual and group activities are included to reinforce student learning.

Table of Contents

Having escaped immediate permanent incapacitation, the turkeys were overjoyed!

You may have made the connection once you got down to problem #8 on the **Doublespeak Thought Experiment**. In the caption above, we find the term "immediate permanent incapacitation," which is doublespeak for "death." No wonder the turkeys were overjoyed! Plus, as you will soon see, the choice of the turkeys is a little play on a form of doublespeak we will look at called gobbledygook.

The terms used in the **Doublespeak Thought Experiment** are good examples of the kind of doublespeak used in our society and even worldwide. So what is doublespeak exactly? **Doublespeak** is "language which pretends to communicate but doesn't."[1] Its purpose is to disguise meaning and to mislead, distort, inflate, or deny responsibility. The danger of doublespeak is that it is designed to alter our perception of reality, and it corrupts our thinking. It also breeds suspicion and distrust. Unfortunately, it is so common that we tend to filter it out; for example if you were online reading MSNBC and you ran into this lead-in to an article found on the next page, would you have been surprised by the use of the term "food insecurity" or would you have read it without taking notice?

1. William Lutz, "The World of Doublespeak," *The State of Language*, ed. Christopher Ricks and Leonard Michaels (University of California Press, 1990), 254.